TOP SECRET
Worcestershire

Michael Layton

Steve Burns

TOP SECRET
Worcestershire

Stephen Burrows & Michael Layton

BREWIN BOOKS

BREWIN BOOKS
56 Alcester Road,
Studley,
Warwickshire,
B80 7LG
www.brewinbooks.com

Published by Brewin Books 2018

A CIP catalogue record for this book is available from the British Library.

ISBN: 978-1-85858-581-9

Printed and bound in Great Britain
by Bell & Bain Ltd.

Contents

Other books by Michael Layton and Stephen Burrows

Joint:
Historical Crime Fiction:
Black Over Bill's Mother's – a storm is coming
Keep Right On

Non-Fiction:
The Noble Cause
Walsall's Front Line – Volume One (1997-1998)
Top Secret Worcestershire

By Michael Layton
Non-Fiction:
Hunting the Hooligans
Tracking the Hooligans
Police Dog Heroes
Birmingham's Front Line
Violence in the Sun
The Night The Owl Cried – A Taste of Cyprus
The Hooligans Are Still Among Us

Facebook Page: 'Bostin Books' – www.facebook.com/BostinBooks

Dedication

We dedicate this book to the brilliance, courage and dedication of all who worked in whatever capacity at the various Malvern research establishments, Defford and Pershore Airfields, and their later research facilities. Whilst the full story of the work and achievements at these establishments may never come to light, there is no doubt that without these people, the independence and security of the United Kingdom could have been lost, both in World War Two and thereafter.

* * *

Also to our wives, Andry and Sue, who put up with, and support, the writing and research.

Author Biographies

Michael Layton QPM joined the British Transport Police as a Cadet on the 1st September 1968 and, after three years, was appointed as a Police Constable, serving at Birmingham New Street Station. In 1972 he transferred to Birmingham City Police, which amalgamated in 1974 to become the West Midlands Police, where he eventually reached the rank of Chief Superintendent in 1997. On retirement from that Force in 2003 he went on to see service with the Sovereign Bases Police in Cyprus, and then returned to the British Transport Police in 2004, initially as a Detective Superintendent (Director of Intelligence), and then in his last two years as the Operations Superintendent at Birmingham, where he continued with his passion for combating football violence, until finally retiring again in 2011. In the January 2003 New Year's Honours List he was awarded the Queens Police Medal for distinguished police service. He is the co-author of a book entitled *'Hunting the Hooligans – the true story of Operation Red Card'* which was published in July 2015 by Milo Books, and the author of *'Violence in the Sun – a History of Football Violence in Cyprus'* which was published as an EBook also by Milo in May 2015. He has also co-authored/authored *'Tracking the Hooligans – A history of football violence on the UK rail network'* by Amberley Publishers, *'Police Dog Heroes – a history of the British Transport Police Dog Section'*, and *'Birmingham's Front Line – True Police Stories'* also by Amberley. In May 2017 *'The Hooligans Are Still Among Us'* was released also by Amberley, and the following month *'The Night The Owl Cried – A Taste of Cyprus'*, co-authored with Androulla Christou-Layton was released. Michael has been working with Stephen Burrows and they have co-authored *'Black over Bill's Mother's'*, a historical crime fiction book, a sequel, *'Keep Right On'*, and non-fiction books, *'The Noble Cause – policing in the West Midlands in the 80s/90s'*, *'Walsall's Front Line Volume I'* and *'Top Secret Worcestershire'*. Michael is a self-employed consultant whose specialism is crime and community safety.

* * *

Stephen Burrows joined West Midlands Police in 1983, working in Birmingham, Wolverhampton and Walsall. He performed a wide variety of roles in ranks up to and including Detective Superintendent. These included uniform command, complaints and discipline (including internal and cross force enquiries) and CID command (including Serious Crime Investigation, Child Protection and Head of Intelligence).

In 2002 he transferred to Warwickshire Police as Chief Superintendent (Area Commander), then became Detective Chief Superintendent (Head of Crime) for the force, a post held for 5 years. He was trained as Senior Investigating Officer, in Kidnap command, and all levels of Firearms Command amongst other skills. He retired in 2013 following thirty years' service, eleven of which were spent at Chief Superintendent rank. He currently works for The Home Office in the field of Communications Data.

The author's first joint venture with Michael Layton was a historical crime fiction novel, called *'Black Over Bill's Mother's'*, followed by two joint non-fiction books recounting policing experiences in Birmingham and Walsall, *'The Noble Cause'*, and *'Walsall's Front Line – Volume One'*. A sequel to *'Black Over Bill's Mother's'*, entitled *'Keep Right On'* was published in Spring 2017, followed by *'Top Secret Worcestershire.'*

Foreword

by Dr Chris Pell FIET FRAeS BSc CEng
(Former Chief Scientist of the Royal Air Force)

AT AN initial glance, the casual reader might be forgiven for asking: what was the Defford airfield and what possible interest and significance might, today, be attached to a fairly remote, nearly deserted and disused rural Worcestershire airfield?

The authors of this fascinating book, Stephen Burrows and Michael Layton, provide the answer to that question by giving the reader an informed, human and revealing historical account, describing the supremely important contribution the Defford and Pershore airfields provided to the defence of the United Kingdom, most particularly during the darkest days of World War Two, and their unique role working with the *'boffins'* of Malvern.

In some sense, it is almost a Cinderella story. A considerable quantity of information exists in the public domain about the earlier history of radar in the United Kingdom such as the initial radar experiments in 1935, through the research at Worth Matravers, the famous operational *'Chain Home'* radar system, to the acclaimed radar research groups formed at the Telecommunications Research Establishment at Malvern, Worcestershire in 1942.

What might easily be overlooked and forgotten, however, is the task of the substantial experimental flying of the *'boffins' kit'* as a critical prerequisite to developing the advanced technology, basically in order to make it work satisfactorily, but equally importantly to ensure its timely and successful deployment into operational service.

As the authors clearly and effectively show, these tasks were not only technologically and logistically challenging, they were also done at great personal risks associated with experimental flying.

It is a story of supreme efforts by pilots, ground crew, scientists, engineers and rafts of support staff, both female and male. The intimate and critical involvement of industry and universities is also recognised.

The authors fairly inform the reader that this book is not a scientific or extensive technology treatise. However, any book concerned with aspects of radar cannot exclude technical accounts, such as the H2S ground-mapping radar and the University of Birmingham magnetron, which allowed such radars to be constructed.

The book includes technical angles such as these but it also achieves a good balance between the science and the human aspects, recounting many personal stories in detail. It is an important complement to any technical treatise, hopefully encouraging readers to investigate the science in further detail.

It is a major contribution towards helping us all to gain knowledge of, and to retain, a historical record of the challenging, selfless and, at times, courageous multi-disciplined defence work undertaken by individuals and teams.

Above all else it is a true record of how people and science came together to make the world a better and more secure place in which to live.

Introduction

DEEP IN the beautiful Worcestershire countryside lie a number of secret places that played a special part in protecting a generation from the onslaught of a world war. The legacy of their work continues to protect generations to this day.

A clue to the secret past might be glimpsed by a traveller passing through leafy Worcestershire lanes, their eyes caught by a structure that seems out of place against the backdrop of fields and hills – the dish of a gigantic radio telescope.

How did such an incongruous structure arrive in the middle of nowhere, and what does it do?

This book answers the question, and recounts the dramatic history of two 'Top Secret' wartime airfields, including the one upon which the telescope is situated, and how their activities were inextricably linked to the 'boffins' of the Malvern Telecommunications Research Establishment.

It tells the story of brilliant inventions, wartime courage and sacrifice, tragic air crashes, and ordinary and extraordinary people, pushing themselves and their machines as far as they could go – to the limit and beyond.

Crafted using the recollections of some of those individuals, and members of their families, the book examines the qualities that set them apart from others and made them special, and the truly exceptional wartime commitment and camaraderie that fuelled extraordinary endeavour and achievement.

Their recollections are brought alive by numerous images, many from private individuals touched in some way by the secret places and secret work, the majority not previously published.

* * *

The Malvern Hills run from the south of the county of Worcestershire into Herefordshire, and are now designated as an area of outstanding natural beauty. The Worcestershire Beacon, which at 425m is the highest point in the county, lies within this range. Many *'boffins'* recalled that a walk on the hills was a good way of clearing the mind whilst wrestling with a seemingly intractable scientific problem.

Malvern is a quiet spa town nestling on the side of the Malvern Hills, its 'waters' attracting much interest and popularity during the Victorian era. The town itself was founded in the 11th century when Benedictine monks established a priory at the foot of the highest peak of the Malvern Hills.

During the 19th century Malvern grew in size as it became popular as a hydrotherapy spa based on its famous spring waters.

Towards the end of that century the town's focus shifted to education, with the establishment of several private boarding schools in former hotels and large villas.

The relocation of the Telecommunications Research Establishment (TRE) to Malvern in 1942, recounted in Chapter Two, dramatically changed the profile and character of the town.

* * *

Defford is a small and ancient village in Worcestershire located between the towns of Pershore and Upton-On-Severn. It was mentioned in the Domesday Book. Historically it has been a rural farming area and sits twelve miles south of Worcester.

A century ago, local market gardeners and fruit growers used to take their goods to the Defford Railway Station, from thence transported for sale in industrial cities. The station is no longer there. The village itself proudly hosts a memorial to the Telecommunications Flying Unit, referred to in the final chapter.

* * *

Pershore is a market town set in the heart of the Vale of Evesham, situated nine miles from Worcester, and also featured in Domesday as *'Old English Persh'*.

It features a medieval Abbey, today dominated by a pinnacled tower, from the top of which one can see Bredon Hill. At nearly 1,000 feet high this is the largest outlying hill of the Cotswolds and forms a ridge to one side of Defford Airfield. A folly in the form of a tower sits on the summit, Parsons Folly.

A short distance from the town-centre stands Pershore Old Bridge, which was the scene of fighting during the Civil War, and was taken out of service for road traffic in 1926.

The town sits on the banks of the River Avon, and plums and pears are grown locally. The town now boasts an annual *'Plum Festival'*.

* * *

During the course of World War Two, the County of Worcestershire played host to a number of RAF establishments, all of which were important in their own way.

RAF Worcester was originally the world's first Municipal Airport in the 1920s and was requisitioned in 1939, becoming No 2 Elementary Flying Training School (EFTS) between 1940 and 1945.

Tiger Moths, as well as Fairey Battle fighter-bombers, which were built some twenty miles away at Longbridge, flew from the airfield.

The grass airfield was used on occasions to facilitate crash landings. In one such landing in September 1942, a Douglas Dakota transport plane, which had taken off from RAF Pershore, crash-landed and finished up in Worcester's rubbish dump. The actor Clark Gable was on board with a film crew doing a gunnery training film. In 1945, the RAF left the site, which was until 1947 used to house German prisoners of war.

* * *

RAF Berrow was operational between 1941 and May 1945, and was used as a Satellite Landing Ground, (SLG), consisting of a grass airstrip and a number of buildings. The airfield also provided additional storage for a number of RAF maintenance units.

Parts of the airfield were camouflaged using poles similar to those seen in hop fields with a covering of wire wool that was painted green.

Planes were hidden under these screens prior to being delivered to operational squadrons.

Nearby a GCI, (Ground Controlled Interception), radar station was operated by Malvern's Telecommunications Research Establishment and aircraft engaged in radar testing sometimes landed there.

* * *

Close to the village of Wick, near Pershore, was RAF Comberton, a GCI radar station. It was one of five inland bases used to detect and track enemy aircraft.

It initially operated using temporary accommodation, and trucks with transmitter and receiver aerials on gantries some 67m apart. In 1943 the station was then upgraded with proper buildings and was classed as an Air Ministry Experimental Station (AMES). They were equipped with long-range fixed radar which was able to track several aircraft at the same time.

After the war, RAF Comberton became a 'ROTOR' station, which was a United Kingdom air defence radar system set up to counter the potential threat from the Soviet Union.

* * *

RAF Hartlebury, near Kidderminster, hosted No 25 Maintenance Unit from 1938 until well after the end of World War Two. The majority of staff there were civilian personnel, and it was used to store and distribute material for the RAF, at home and overseas, including Spitfire spare parts and Fire Engines.

* * *

RAF Honeybourne was in operation between 1941 and 1946 and was a base for No 24 Operations Training Unit (OTU), which trained Canadian aircrew to fly Vickers Wellington bombers and Armstrong Whitworth Whitleys. In keeping with other training units it also engaged in bombing raids and leaflet dropping exercises. By the end of 1944 it was home to over two thousand men and women.

During the war years RAF Honeybourne was also home to the Ferry Training Unit and No 1425 (Communications) Flight.

It was later used to store aircraft prior to decommissioning, before finally closing in 1947.

* * *

In 1939, the War Office requisitioned 105 acres of land in Wythall to construct what became known as RAF Wythall, ten miles from the town of Bromsgrove. It became home to No 6 Barrage Balloon Centre, whose purpose was to protect parts of Birmingham, Coventry and the Black Country from aerial attack, a 600 square mile area.

Barrage balloons were known as *'blimps'* and were designed to disrupt the efforts of the German Luftwaffe by placing an airborne obstruction between them and their ground targets.

At the end of the war the station initially became No 105 Personnel Despatch Centre, (WAAF), Wythall, a *'demob'* centre for servicewomen, before accommodating the Radar Navigation Aids Wing for a year in 1952.

After being used as a specialist centre for linguists, the station finally became non-operational at the end of 1959.

* * *

Worcestershire was home to many thousands of service personnel, both men and women, during the war years. Whilst much of the infrastructure of their bases has long been gone their memories persist. This book records in words, and photographs, what part Defford, Pershore and Malvern played in creating history.

The early days of Radar
Radar runs like a golden thread through this story.

Malvern hosted the *'boffins'*, the scientists who developed radar into electronic-based weapon systems that played a major part in winning World War Two.

From Defford and Pershore flew pilots that tested the equipment, and those early radar days were the basis for the new science of Radio Astronomy and modern weapons systems. The rest of this introductory chapter sets the scene by telling, in a summary manner, the fascinating story of radar prior to its arrival at Malvern.

* * *

The discovery of the principles of radar, at least for the United Kingdom, was rather bizarrely born from an investigation requested of the Radio Research Station in Slough in 1935, of the possibility of constructing a *'death ray'* using huge amounts of radio (electromagnetic) energy to damage an aircraft and/or its crew.

The idea of death rays was popular at the time and there were many claims from 'inventors' that they had solved this conundrum. In fact a prize of £1,000 was offered to anyone who could kill a sheep at 100 yards – it was never paid out and the flocks remained unmolested!

It was quickly concluded that the generation of the required energy was impossible. However, A F Wilkins, the Assistant calculating the possibility, concluded that if an aircraft flew through a beam of radio waves it would deflect back to the ground sufficient energy to enable detection. His suggestion was backed with £10,000 of a worried government's money to develop the idea. The British were desperate to find a way of tracking bombers as the mantra until then had been, *'the bomber will always get through'*.

On 26 February 1935, a demonstration using the BBC Daventry radio transmitter proved the concept. A Heyford bomber was flown up and down the radio beam transmitted by the mast, and radio-receiving equipment installed in a van was able to detect the aircraft at a distance of up to eight miles. This was probably the first demonstration of what today is known as *'passive radar'*.

The first dedicated experimental radar was constructed at Orfordness in Suffolk, and in June 1935, radar echoes were obtained from a flying-boat at a range of seventeen miles, quickly extended to forty, and then eighty miles by the end of 1935.

In 1936, the Orfordness group was moved to Bawdsey Manor, also in Suffolk, and A.P. Rowe, a young scientist of later considerable scientific fame, became the Superintendent.

The success of the 1935 experiments led to an unprecedented sum of £10,000,000 in government funds being granted to build five radar stations to help defend the approaches to the Thames Estuary, completed in 1938.

These were followed, by Easter 1939, by a chain, known as 'Chain Home', of ground-based radar stations covering the east and south coasts from Ventnor, Isle of Wight, to the Firth of Tay. These stations were integrated with Fighter Command and both the radar and its close integration with RAF fighter planes were later to prove crucial in the 'Battle of Britain' and the 'Blitz'.

When war broke out, the Bawdsey site and the scientists were felt to be vulnerable to attack.

This was not without reason, as on 2 August 1939, prior to the outbreak of war, the Graf Zeppelin airship spied on Bawdsey in an effort to monitor radar transmissions.

The staff at Bawdsey were re-located to Dundee in early September 1939, bearing the name Air Ministry Research Establishment, (AMRE). Unfortunately the facilities proved to be very unsuitable for the hundreds of staff and this remained a problem for some twelve months.

A young scientist, (Sir) Bernard Lovell, was by this time arriving at Dundee, to be told to report to E.G. Bowen at Scone, near Perth, to work on AI (Air Interception radar). In a remarkable and fortunate piece of intuition, the 'Tizard Committee', the Air Defence Committee formed in 1935, had foreseen the requirement for airborne interception radar years before the outbreak of war.

They also predicted that the integration of ground radar with fighter deployment would contribute significantly to the defeat of the enemy daylight bombers, resulting in a switch to night bombing, and this is precisely what happened in the winter of 1940-1.

At night, visual identification of an enemy aircraft by a fighter pilot was around 1,000 feet or less and the 'Chain Home' system was incapable of providing that level of precision.

Thus, the committee commissioned the development of a miniature radar system, (AI or Airborne Interception), that could be placed into a night fighter, allowing target acquisition from a range of around four miles.

This work had been given to Bowen at Bawdsey, and he had subsequently developed an experimental 1.5 metre wavelength radar that he had been ordered to fit into thirty Blenheim night fighters by 1 September 1939.

The task took no cognizance of the resources available to Bowen and was made more difficult by the hurried move to Dundee.

Hitherto, Bowen had used the RAF aerodrome at Martlesham Heath, well-equipped and nearby for testing, but in Scotland he was informed that he would be using Perth airfield, at Scone. This was a small civilian aerodrome contracted to RAF Training Command for training in light aircraft, and it was soon recognized that a move to a larger airfield with the required facilities would be necessary.

The 'Mark I', 1.5 metre, AI Radar that Bowen had developed had serious limitations in terms of its maximum and minimum ranges. The maximum range problem stemmed from the broad beam of the 1.5 metre system. This 'floodlit' the terrain area in front of the fighter and resultant ground echoes limited the range at which night fighters could locate enemy aircraft.

The key to an effective airborne radar was to narrow the antenna beam commensurate with 'microwave' frequency, i.e. to a wavelength of ten centimeters, but there was no way of producing the high power required.

Throughout the winter of 1939-40 dispute raged as to the merits of evolving 1.5 metre radar as opposed to progressing the reduction of the wavelength.

Sir Bernard Lovell recalled, 'a see-saw existence', being directed between working on 1.5 metre AI and the development of smaller wavelengths to allow miniaturization.

Lovell realised that getting the AI equipment to work whilst airborne was a vastly more difficult challenge than improving 1.5 metre ground radar.

The sinking of the HMS Royal Oak battleship by U-Boat U47 in Scapa Flow on 14 October 1939, with the loss of 899 lives, underlined the importance of being able to detect both enemy aircraft and submarines and this demanded airborne radar.

The unsuitability of airfield and laboratory facilities at Scone led to the move of Bowen's airborne radar group to St Athan, near Barry in South Wales, on 1 November 1939.

This was in fact a regressive move as St Athan was unfinished and had no facilities at all. The group were given a huge hanger to work in, with no heating, and had to try and work in gloves, hats and overcoats.

Bowen observed that this cutting edge technology for the RAF was being developed in conditions worse than a *'prison farm'*.

There were already four thousand staff at St Athan and every building was overflowing. Unhelpfully, the main research facility remained in Dundee, three hundred miles away. To underline the fallacy of the move, a Junkers 88 dropped a 1000 lb bomb on the main runway a few weeks after Bowen's arrival.

Luckily it failed to explode, bouncing along the runway like a tennis ball. Had it detonated, the story of airborne radar could have been very different, as Lovell and Bowen could have lost their lives.

Now another distraction from the pursuit of AI appeared, a direct result of development work on AI that had produced clear echoes from vessels at sea. This had been further developed with great success in detecting larger vessels. This became known as ASV (Air to Surface Vessel).

Soon after their arrival at St Athan, Bowen's group was ordered to prioritise the fitting of ASV units into Hudson and Sunderland aircraft. This was because the German pocket battleship *'Deutschland'*, a thorn in the side of Allied shipping, had been able to return to Germany via the English Channel without detection by the Navy, Fleet Air Arm or Coastal Command. It was believed that ASV would have enabled its pinpointing and destruction.

Work was diverted into fitting ASV units, and this delayed any further research into AI until February 1940, ultimately leading to the dispersal of Bowen's group and the re-forming of a research group on the Dorset coast.

* * *

On 7 May 1940, both the Dundee, and elements of the St Athan's research groups arrived at Worth Matravers on the South Coast near Swanage, with use of an airfield at Christchurch.

The new unit was called MAPRE (Ministry of Aircraft Production Research Establishment).

The 'airfield', however, turned out to be a small private airfield with no hangers, a wooden hut containing two light aircraft, a closed café and a flying club room. Houses surrounded the airfield, so extensions to the runways were impossible.

Fig 1 *TRE Worth Matravers circa 1940*

The experimental radar flying unit had to cope with these difficult and dangerous conditions, which were unsuitable for Blenheim night fighters, for eighteen months, until the airfield at Hurn opened, although this proved to be a short-lived arrangement as the move to Defford was enforced in 1942.

A new team of scientists was formed at Worth Matravers, to focus upon AI radar development.

Three days later Germany invaded Holland and Belgium, Chamberlain was replaced by Churchill as Prime Minister, and the British Expeditionary Force began their retreat towards Dunkirk. The pressure to develop AI was intensified, but the lack of a solution to the generation of the power output required for 10cm radar was still a seemingly insurmountable barrier.

The answer lay in Birmingham, with the invention of a device that can truly be said to have changed the course of World War Two, the *'resonant cavity magnetron'*.

The resonant cavity magnetron

The cavity magnetron has been called *'the invention that changed the world'*, and it was invented locally, at Birmingham University.

It was a complete 'game-changer' in the development of radar, both during and long after the War, and it is no understatement to say that this device played a significant, if not crucial part in achieving Allied victory in World War Two.

It was classified as 'Top Secret', and Churchill himself authorised that it be flown to the United States and gifted to Britain's allies in a highly secret wartime mission.

Once operational, measures were taken to make sure that the device did not fall into Nazi hands by the placing of explosive charges on magnetron units in the event of aircraft crashing in occupied Europe.

In fact the Germans were astonished when they found a microwave cavity magnetron inside a crashed Pathfinder bomber from a raid on Cologne, on 2 February 1943, after the explosive charge had failed to go off.

And yet, a direct descendant of the original highly secret cavity magnetron is present in nearly every house in Britain, secreted within the humble microwave oven.

This device was the core of the pioneering radar units that guided the bombers that destroyed Germany, and the RAF fighter planes and Royal Navy vessels that intercepted German aircraft, ships and U-Boats.

The resonant cavity magnetron is a generator of high frequency electromagnetic radiation. The science behind its discovery is too complex for the purposes of this book, but the history of its invention is crucial to the events that took place at Malvern, Defford and subsequently at Pershore.

The key event in the history of the magnetron was the appointment, in 1937, of M.L.E Oliphant to the Poynting Professorship of Physics, and Headship of the Department of Physics at the University of Birmingham. Until his arrival the department had only conducted small-scale research but he focused it towards nuclear physics.

Oliphant's first senior recruit was J.T. Randall who had already excelled at GEC laboratories in the field of luminescence, the emission of light by a substance without the application of heat, stemming from chemical reactions, stress on a crystal, sub-atomic motions or electrical energy. Oliphant set up a luminescence laboratory at Birmingham.

A young research scientist by the name of H.A.H Boot joined the department in 1939 in order to experiment with a small high voltage accelerator for neutrons, a sub-atomic particle.

Later in 1939, a third member associated with the invention of the magnetron, J. Sayers, joined them.

During the turbulent months of 1939 preceding the outbreak of war, Oliphant set to thinking about how his department could help the war-effort.

Due to his senior position he had been given information concerning the development of 'radio-direction finding', (RDF), later known as 'radio direction and range', (Radar), under Watson-Watt at Bawdsey in Suffolk.

Oliphant quickly realized that the limitations of these systems were due to their long wavelength i.e. 10 metres or more.

Radar works by transmitting electromagnetic waves, often in the form of pulses, via a transmitter and aerial system. The pulse strikes a distant object and a very small fraction of the transmit power is reflected back to a receiver. The range is measured by the time interval between transmission and reception, and the direction by the angle of the aerial system that delivers maximum response. Angular precision depends upon the ratio of the wavelength used to the size of the aerial.

The higher the frequency used then, in general, a shorter pulse can be used and that is good for resolving target features and locating them accurately.

So, from the viewpoint of precision, high frequency/short wavelength is optimum.

The chain of radar stations around the South and East coasts of England at the commencement of war in 1939, were capable of detecting aircraft at 15,000 feet altitude, and up to a range of 150 miles operating at a wavelength of ten to thirteen metres, (23-30MHz).

As described, airborne radar was being tested at a wavelength of 1.5 metres (200MHz) but, even at this reduced wavelength, there were difficulties in the size of the equipment for airborne use, together with its power and sensitivity.

It was already appreciated in 1939 that much shorter wavelengths could deliver considerable increases in range, precision and sensitivity, but there was no device able to transmit the required power together with increased receiver sensitivity at such short wavelengths. What was needed were high-power transmitters at much shorter wavelengths, but contemporary valve technology could not deliver the power required.

However, it was known that linear and cyclic accelerators for nuclear physics delivered such high power, albeit not at the required short wavelengths.

Oliphant was brought into Britain's *'Top Secret'* radar program and made a pre-war journey to the USA to view the work of Ernest Lawrence, the cyclotron physicist, in California, and assessed a new 'klystron' generator of short wavelength power developed at Stanford University by the Varian brothers.

The klystron is a microwave tube where an electron beam is passed through one or more resonant cavities, without requiring a magnetic field for its operation.

Oliphant returned bearing the technical information to enable a klystron to be built at Birmingham and began focusing on the potential of using this device to deliver sufficient power at a wavelength of 10cm in order to render airborne radar possible.

A group of physicists from Birmingham were sent to familiarise themselves with the operation and limitations of the *'Chain Home'* system at Ventnor, Isle of Wight, and other coastal stations.

The main problem was *'ground return echoes'*, which arose because long wavelength radar antennas could not be made highly directional and as a result the strong radar echo from the ground obscured the very weak echo from a plane beyond a certain range.

Oliphant declared that there was a requirement for an oscillator tube that developed a peak power minimum of 1kilowatt at a 10cm or less wavelength.

Such short wavelength, known as *'microwaves'*, had three advantages: image resolution would be far better; equipment, particularly the antenna, would be much smaller, allowing easier installation into aircraft and naval vessels; and the improved directional accuracy microwave antenna delivered would remove the ground echo problem and grant greater range.

Subsequently, the Admiralty, responsible for coordinating the development of electron tubes, which were known as 'valves' in the UK, for all military services, contracted Birmingham University to develop microwave generators and detectors.

An electron tube is a sealed glass bulb containing two or more electrodes: used to generate, amplify, and rectify electric oscillations and alternating currents.

This commission had the unanticipated and beneficial effect of keeping Birmingham's physics department intact whilst other establishment's physicists were split up and sent to various Government laboratories.

Early in 1940, the Admiralty contract group of security-cleared scientists and staff occupied the recently completed Nuffield building at Birmingham University.

Hours of work were rigorous with only every third Saturday free, and 'The Official Secrets Act' was signed by all concerned.

The group initially concentrated on the development of high-powered klystrons as microwave generators.

In a 1977 interview H.A.H Boot recalled that upon his return to Birmingham from Ventnor,

> 'The team had already been arranged and was already working on klystrons ...Randall wasn't doing anything much then, and I came back and I wasn't doing anything much. And we were just put together.'

Meanwhile the klystron team had succeeded in not only building one to the American design, but achieved an output power of 100 watts at 7.5cm wavelength.

They conducted field tests at the Air Ministry Research Establishment, (AMRE) at Worth Matravers in July 1940.

The equipment successfully detected aircraft using a continuing wave mode with an output of 40 watts at 7.5cm wavelength.

It was also apparent that without considerable development the equipment could not be made small enough to fit into an aircraft – meanwhile the magnetron had been invented.

The creation of the magnetron began in late 1939 when Randall and Boot concluded that the magnetron was much more likely than the klystron to generate high power from a practical vacuum tube/valve electronic device.

In November 1939, with guidance and suggestions from Oliphant, Randall and Boot worked on combining the klystron and magnetron capabilities. In an afternoon's discussion they worked out the basic design of the multi-cavity magnetron, the type of cavity resonator, the number of cavities and the form of output circuit.

The prototype magnetron was first tested on 21 February 1940. Immediately it was apparent that a great deal of power was being generated. Neon lamps could be lit some distance from the tube and cigarettes lit from the output lead. A number of car headlamps were burnt out trying to estimate the power produced.

The next few days were spent measuring, with the surprising result that the device was found to be producing 400 watts at 9.8cm. This microwave power output, and the subsequent increases obtained, considerably exceeded expectations.

The prototype had to be converted into a production, sealed-off tube, and the General Electric Company, (GEC), staff, led by E.C.S. Megaw, improved the original experimental version and evolved the very first production magnetron.

Megaw engineered a number of important changes to the original design and by August 1940, magnetron E1189 version number 12, a revised design with eight rather than six cavities, was producing 10kw.

* * *

This magnetron that was taken to the United States in September 1940, was described in an official account of the American Office of Scientific Research and Development as *'the most valuable cargo ever brought to our shores'*.

In early 1940, Sir Henry Tizard, British scientist and chair of the Aeronautical Research Committee – which had supported radar development, suggested that Britain should disclose its scientific secrets in the military arena to the then neutral USA, and Canada, in exchange for much needed help in technology and production.

After initial misgivings, Churchill agreed on 9 August 1940, and the mission set off with magnetron E1189 number 12 in a metal box containing other secrets including Frank Whittle's jet-engine, a paper on the feasibility of the atomic bomb, designs for rockets, superchargers, gyroscopic gunsights, submarine detection devices, self-sealing fuel tanks and plastic explosives.

In a quintessentially British cameo, E.G. Bowen, the radar expert who carried the device to North America, kept the *'Top Secret'* magnetron in its metal case under his London hotel bed – and nearly lost it at Euston Station when an overzealous porter took it from him!

The Tizard mission arrived in Halifax, Canada, on 6 September 1940 and went to Washington six days later.

It is clear that the magnetron stole the show, and Bowen recalled that when it was first disclosed on 19 September, the Americans had nothing to match the magnetron and were stunned when shown it produced 10 kilowatts of pulsed power at a wavelength of 10 centimetres.

The American Secretary of War noted that his scientists had told him that the Magnetron was allowing them to catch up on two years work and far outweighed anything the USA could give Britain.

The magnetron was subsequently disclosed to the Canadians and both they, and the Americans, used it as the basis for their own radar developments.

The disclosure and gift of this groundbreaking device persuaded both future allies of the bona-fides of the British, and paved the way for the immense amount of scientific cooperation that took place subsequently, one example of which is recounted later in this book – the tale of the *'self-landing'* Boeing.

The impact of the magnetron is demonstrated by a note from a participant in British testing of the device for airborne interception radar that he felt it would be revolutionary for radar for all three military services.

* * *

It would be remiss to conclude this section without mention of some of the other 'spin-offs' of Oliphant's Birmingham University group research.

The *'Birmingham klystron'* was further developed after the war by the Stanford team who had originally evolved its design. They overcame a number of technical problems to develop the klystron to produce high-pulsed power, originally for use in linear accelerators. Today the klystron, in both continuous wave and pulsed versions has widespread use. Low-power klystrons are used as oscillators in terrestrial microwave relay communications links, while high-power klystrons are used as output tubes in UHF television transmitters, satellite communication, and radar transmitters, and to generate the drive power for modern particle accelerators.

Oliphant also tasked a group with looking at receivers and general circuits and one member, R. Kompfner, conceived a device known as the *'travelling wave tube'*, which produces high bandwidths with low noise.

It is now widely used in terrestrial and satellite microwave linkages, including in spacecraft and electronic warfare systems and in radar transmitters and receivers.

It is the story of the resonant cavity magnetron however, that dominated the development of radar in which both Malvern, Defford and subsequently Pershore, played crucial roles.

Fig 2 Early 'S Band' 10cm Cavity Magnetron

Fig 3 Low power Klystron used as receiver oscillator

The resonant cavity magnetron totally transformed the viability, practicality and performance of almost all types of radar for decades to come.

* * *

On 19 July 1940, the first GEC-engineered production *'sealed-off unit'* cavity magnetron arrived at Worth Matravers.

In the meantime Lovell had been successfully working on the construction and use of *'paraboloids'* in radar antennae.

In layperson's terms, a parabolic antenna is the now familiar 'dish' reflector used in radar devices – the dish shape being a paraboloid.

The main advantage of a parabolic dish is that it enables high directivity of the radio waves in a narrow transmission beam, or it can receive radio waves from one direction only. It also bestows the highest 'gain', meaning that it can produce the narrowest beam-widths of any antenna type.

To do so the dish needs to be much larger than the wavelength used, thus the marriage of the parabolic dish, and the magnetron that enabled a 'microwave' 10cm wavelength, produced the potential for apparatus small enough to fit into an aircraft.

On 12 August 1940, the magnetron was successfully paired with a paraboloid antennae and the first echoes from aircraft were picked up on the 10cm wavelength.

The next day the equipment picked up echoes from an assistant carrying a sheet of metal whilst cycling. This should have been impossible due to ground echoes but the importance of the test result was not immediately realised.

Now the war intervened once more, as the Luftwaffe, having been defeated in daytime, switched to night bombing, and Churchill issued an invasion alert on 22 September.

The research unit looked increasingly vulnerable – situated next to a likely target, a *'Chain Home'* station, and in fact enemy bombers often flew overhead. They were moved to a school at nearby Langton Matravers, their last move before the historic switch to Malvern and Defford. In the meantime there were further diversions from concentrating on airborne radar in the form of the

AGLT (Automatic Gun Laying Turret) and using 10cm radar for detecting submarines from ships.

The AGLT work was eventually taken over by an American system, but by March 1941 fully engineered 10cm sets for ships were on sea trials following impressive test results at Swanage. By May 1942, two hundred and thirty-six ships fitted with 10cm radar were at sea detecting German U-Boats including targets as small as their conning towers.

Meanwhile the Luftwaffe were bombing at night almost unimpeded.

The existing 1.5 metre AI radar in Beaufighter aircraft had some success once it was paired with the 'Ground Controlled Interception' (GCI) system that used a 'plan position indicator' (PPI) that displayed both the radar echo from the target, and the night fighter, allowing ground control to direct the fighter within AI detection distance.

German 'sortie' losses began to mount; at times reaching 10%, and by May 1941 the first phase of massed German night bombings ended.

Attention now returned to 10cm airborne interception radar using the cavity magnetron, together with an ingenious spinning spiral scanner so smooth that when running at full speed it caused barely a ripple in a glass of water standing on its framework.

This device apparently caused consternation when first viewed, as the eccentric rotation of the scanner at lower speeds gave the impression that it had *'the one apparent desire of escaping from the aircraft altogether'* (A.P Rowe). It proved to be extremely reliable however.

It is beyond the scope of this book to detail the numerous scientific problems overcome during the development of 10cm AI, by ingenious scientists under the pressure of war.

In March 1941 the first tests of *'centimetre'* (10cm) AI took place using a Blenheim.

Contact with a target 1-2 miles distant at less than a mile height was immediately achieved, rising quickly to 3 miles and subsequently to ranges of up to 10 miles.

By July 1941 'centimetre' AI was ordered to be fitted into a squadron of Beaufighters for operational use.

This required another form of genius to 'operationalise' the often delicate equipment produced by the 'boffins'.

The credit for the creation of the final production quality operational centimetre units of 1942, and 1943, lay with GEC research laboratories.

By December 1942, centimetre AI equipped Beaufighters had destroyed one hundred enemy bombers and the equipment was also being fitted in Mosquito and DeHavilland fighters.

By autumn 1941, with the 'Battle of Britain' won, German night-bombing of British cities all but ended due to British night-time fighter supremacy, and with the threat of invasion receding another task central to the story of Malvern and Defford was set.

* * *

On 3 September 1941, Churchill asked the Chief of Air Staff to give urgent attention to the failure of the RAF's own night bombing campaign in Europe.

The problem was fundamental; the British bombers were missing their targets.

On 29 December 1941, Lovell was instructed to cease many months of work on a 'lock-follow' system for AI, and turn his full attention to a 'blind bombing' aid, then known as 'BN' (blind navigation).

The background to this order was that in July 1941, Bomber Command were ordered to direct their main effort towards,

> 'Dislocating the German transportation system and to destroying the morale of the civilian population as a whole, and of industrial workers in particular.' (Vice-Chief of Air Staff 9/7/41).

However, statistical analysis of results showed that whilst Bomber Command believed that they were hitting their targets, in reality two-thirds of planes missed by up to five miles, and little damage was being inflicted.

It emerged that the aircrews knew this and were losing morale because of the effort and danger involved for such poor outcomes. A crucial meeting on 26 October 1941 considered Churchill's urgent request, and its decisions set the course for the later work at Malvern and Defford.

There were in fact two highly successful systems already in operation to assist precision bombing, 'GEE' and 'OBOE'. However both relied upon ground transmissions from England, limiting their range.

GEE was a navigational system that measured pulses from three separate radio transmitters in England to determine aircraft position. The navigator could plot the plane's position using a special chart marked with lattice lines corresponding to 'constant time differences' for transmissions from the three stations.

GEE had the advantage that no transmissions from the aircraft were required, but it was easily jammed and too inaccurate for precision bombing. Its range was limited by the curvature of the earth and could locate and position an aircraft within an elliptical area of six miles by one mile at a range of up to three hundred and fifty miles, which did encompass the Ruhr, seat of much of German industry crucial to their war effort.

OBOE was a precision bombing aid that used two accurately plotted radar stations on the East Coast to send signals to a transponder in the bomber which returned them. This enabled the aircraft's position and speed to be calculated.

The aircraft was directed along a track taking it over the target. It was highly accurate – at 250 miles range an aircraft flying at 30,000 feet could drop bombs to within 120 yards of the target, but OBOE could only operate with one aircraft every ten minutes.

It did achieve good results in the Ruhr by being fitted to Mosquitos that, having identified the target using OBOE, dropped flares for the bombers to follow.

However both these systems were ruled out at the October meeting because their limited range prevented their use deeper into Germany, the bombing of which was deemed key in destroying German industry and civilian morale.

The solution was deemed to be a radar bombing aid, self-contained within the aircraft.

Now the memory of the assistant on the bicycle carrying the sheet of metal, detected by 10cm radar and unimpeded by ground echoes sprang to mind.

A recently modified AI system was tested in November 1941 and detected echoes from Southampton from a height of 5,000 feet. This was followed by a series of tests of various types of aerial and much debate over which worked best.

The new system was code-named 'H2S'.

There is still disagreement as to how the name came about, but the consensus is that it was an abbreviation of 'Home Sweet Home' because it enabled the location of, and homing to, a target.

The alternative is that it refers to Hydrogen Sulphide, (rotten-egg gas), because it was 'stinking' that the system had not been developed earlier due to other priorities being imposed.

* * *

At the end of 1941, testing of H2S for the new generation of heavy, four-engined bombers was ordered.

The new bombers were the Stirling, Halifax and Lancaster, and it was decided, following investigation, that the Halifax offered more potential fixings for the scanner than the others.

For technical reasons to do with beam shape, angle and range, it was decided to mount the scanner in a Perspex cover, a cupola, nicknamed the 'baby's bottom' by aircrew, under the Halifax in the under-turret position.

The test plane was Halifax V9977 which arrived at Hurn airport on 27 March 1942.

This plane would later feature in the single biggest disaster to befall H2S.

The scanner equipment was fitted – no easy matter, as it required racks and cabling within the aircraft, and on 17 April 1942 it was first tested.

Initial results were disappointing, with problems with range and the information on the display. A further complication was a continuing difference in opinion over the use of the klystron or magnetron for H2S.

The pressure to assist Bomber Command with a precision bombing aid was intense, as the strategic aim of Bomber Command had switched to 'de-housing' the majority of the population of fifty-eight of Germany's biggest cities over an eighteen month period.

Thus the perfection of H2S became the highest priority.

On 23 December 1941, EMI were given contracts for the manufacture of fifty H2S units despite the difficulties encountered in testing.

EMI put their best engineers onto the project, led by Alan Blumlein, then regarded as one of the best electrical engineers in the country.

However, testing at Swanage and Hurn was to be abruptly cut short as TRE, and its flying unit, were moved to Malvern and Defford respectively.

'*Top Secret Worcestershire*' had begun.

Chapter One

Defford Airfield – 'The Test-Bed'

Noble beginnings

Defford Airfield and its once extensive buildings were crafted in the shadow of the grandeur of an ancient ancestral seat. The Croome Estate was and is a highly visible statement of hundreds of years of English society. It is easy to imagine the setting contributed towards the bravery of the men and women who worked there in wartime, facing daily life-threatening challenges in order to uphold a set of values that were the antipathy of Naziism.

Undoubtedly, during World War Two in particular, some of the living conditions on the airbase were quite austere, nevertheless the photographs taken at sports days and social events paint a picture of comradeship and team spirit set in the heart of rural Worcestershire – the *'free world'* standing firm against *'the oppressors'* with normality the order of the day whilst the risk of death, or serious injury, lurked constantly in the background, British stoicism in the face of evil.

Those men and women were making their own history in a place that was already full of history.

* * *

Croome Court is the ancestral seat of the Earls of Coventry.

Thomas Coventry was born in 1547 and became a lawyer and a Justice in the Court of Common Pleas during the reign of King James. He purchased Croome D'Abitôt in 1592, having married Margaret Jeffery whose family owned the neighbouring Earls Croome. He was knighted in 1606.

The original core house and grounds date back to the 1640s and the 4th Earl, Gilbert Coventry, made large changes to this house.

In 1751, the 6th Earl, George Coventry, inherited the estate and its Jacobean house at the age of twenty-eight years. He decided to modernize the estate and commissioned the famous landscaper, then relatively unknown, Lancelot 'Capability' Brown, together with Sanderson Miller, a pioneer of Gothic revival architecture and landscape designer, to redesign both the house and grounds. Miller was known for erecting 'follies' and other picturesque garden buildings in estates.

Croome was Brown's first architectural project and is a rare example of this aspect of his work. The house was completed between 1751 and 1752, and together with Hagley Hall is the finest example of Neo-Palladian architecture in Worcestershire. Robert Adam also worked on the interior from 1760 onwards, creating the Tapestry Room, Long Gallery and Library.

Like many other great estates, World War One had a detrimental effect on Croome, beginning its decline.

In 1921, the Croome Estate Trust was established by the 9th Earl of Coventry and the entire estate was placed in the hands of the Trust. This arrangement remains in place almost one hundred years later.

The 9th Earl died in 1930, and the 10th in battle at Givenchy in France, in 1940, whilst serving in the Worcester Regiment.

The creation of Defford airfield

During World War Two, Croome Court, and part of the grounds, was requisitioned by the Ministry of Works and leased to the Dutch Government for a year as a potential refuge for Queen Wilhelmina of the Netherlands, following the Nazi occupation of her country. However the Dutch Royal Family only stayed for two weeks and later emigrated to Canada.

Around half of the estate was designated for a new RAF Station, (to be named after the nearest village of Defford), together with some other fields, and Defford Common. The Worcester/Cheltenham railway line ran along one side of the designated area. Runways and taxiways were laid which were then linked to a main building within Croome Park.

A satellite of Pershore

In May 1941, No 23 Operational Training Unit, (OTU), at RAF Pershore, took over Defford airfield as a satellite field.

On the 26 August 1941, one officer and thirty-three NCOs, and airmen, were sent from Pershore to Defford as work on station defence commenced.

A *'Battle Headquarters'* was built on the east side of the airfield and *'Oakington'* pillboxes were constructed, one of which was twenty yards away from it, near the railway line, and a second south of the east/west runway.

A wartime romance

David Haffenden, who went on to serve in the West Midlands Police, has the following recollection of his parents,

'My father, Walter Royal Haffenden, was born in 1913 and originally came from the Old Kent Road in London. He was known to everyone as "Wally" or "Wal" and never used his middle name.

In the early 1940s, at the beginning of World War Two, he moved up from London and was employed as a civilian aircraft fitter at RAF Defford. He had already been working in the aircraft industry in London and knew his trade

Whilst at Defford he lived at 10 Old Street, Upton on Severn and was the chairman of the darts team at "The Twyning" pub.

My mother was Dorothy Rose Rhodes and was born in 1923. She lived in Caledonia Road, Wolverhampton and worked in the assembly department at Fischer Bearings which later changed its name, but went on to make bearings for the aircraft industry.

On the 8 June 1942, my mother was given permission in writing, by the Minister of Labour and National Service, to leave her job to join the Women's Land Army.

She went to live in the WLA Hostel in Upton on Severn and worked on farms in Pershore as well as others as far away as Gloucester. She loved the work and was known as "Dusty" to her friends there, although obviously "Dot" by my father.

She used to frequent some of the local pubs, including "The Lion", and I believe that she met my father in one of them.

They used to write regularly to each other and my mother would sometimes arrange for someone from the hostel to post her letters through his door. They kept them all afterwards and we still have them in the family.

The letters show the deep affection that they had for one another despite their difficult circumstances, with a war going on.

After the war finished my father continued working at Defford, and my mother carried on in the Women's Land

Fig 4 Walter Haffenden at Defford with what is believed to be a Lancaster rear gun turret in the background

Fig 5 Dorothy Haffenden in Land Army uniform

Army, although her parents wanted her to go back to Wolverhampton.

They married in the autumn of 1948, and my mum's wedding ring cost £14 and five shillings, with a discount.

I was born in 1950 but my father never discussed his work at Defford. He came from a generation when children were there "to be seen but not heard" and never chose to enlighten me about what he had been doing.

After moving from Defford in 1951 he moved to Wolverhampton and got a job in a factory as a foreman where they supplied parts for Concorde's undercarriage.

My father died just before his 90th birthday in 2004, and my mother passed away in 2014. Both of their ashes were scattered on the River Severn at Upton – the place that they had met and fallen in love with each other.'

The 'ultimate price'

Flying training commenced at Defford in September 1941.

The training of aircrew was undertaken in two phases, the first of which was focused at Defford on conversion to the Wellington Bomber from the trainer aircraft flown previously. These pilots then went to Pershore where they received training in bombing, navigation, and air gunnery.

Training was extremely hazardous, and during flights from Defford alone in 1942 there were two fatal Wellington crashes near to the airfield. A staggering 8,195 aircrew from Bomber Command died in accidents during World War Two, many of which occurred during training.

The airfield experienced another serious crash on the 29 March 1942, after a Wellington crashed into a building following engine failure. The crew suffered serious injuries, and some of those on the ground suffered minor injuries.

* * *

At this time there were no WAAF, (Women's Auxiliary Air Force), members at Defford because the facilities were poor. Men were billeted in small huts, without water, and divided into cubicles which contained just a bed. Facilities were spread across the airfield with the washrooms, flight offices and eating facilities in a communal wooded area. Wherever possible trees were left in situ, to provide camouflage. There was mud everywhere and the constant noise of trains passing on the nearby railway line during the night.

On the 14 May 1942 the OTU personnel moved back to Pershore after being told that Defford was to be used for other 'hush-hush' purposes.

On the 18 May 1942 RAF Defford was taken over by the Ministry of Aircraft Production.

Defford becomes the test-bed for the 'boffins'

The development of RAF Defford was part of a much bigger project overseen by Captain Spencer Freeman, who was later awarded the CBE for his efforts.

Malvern had been identified as the new home for the 'boffins', of the Telecommunications Research Establishment, (TRE), (see Chapter 2).

One of the key TRE requirements was that there had to be sufficient elevation to be able to see an aircraft twenty-five miles away, and a well-equipped airfield for the airborne testing 'in anger' of all new scientific equipment created by the 'boffins'. Defford satisfied this criteria. Thus the move of TRE was accompanied by the uprooting of the Telecommunications Flying Unit (TFU) from RAF Hurn to Defford. As huge amounts of fitting and adjusting of equipment occurred on the airfield there was an extra requirement for workshops and other ancillaries.

The TFU originated in 1936 at the Aircraft Armament Experimental Establishment, Martlesham Heath. It was originally called 'D Performance and Test Flight', and then the 'Special Duties Flight'. In November 1941 this Flight merged with another calibrating ground radar and formed the TFU, based at Hurn airfield and working with the TRE who at that stage were based at nearby Swanage.

The TFU also flew as 'targets' for the Air Defence Research and Development Establishment, (ADRDE), that also moved from Christchurch to Pale Manor, Malvern, in May 1942.

ADRDE devised radar systems for controlling searchlights, and anti-aircraft guns, for the Army. TFU also provided testing targets for the Coast Artillery Experimental Establishment which had a detachment at Earls Croome.

* * *

The original airfield at Defford was devoid of buildings and quarters for staff. Over five thousand building workers were brought in to build accommodation for one thousand five hundred RAF personnel, hangers for aircraft, extensive aprons, hard-standing for planes to sit on, and runway extensions. The workers were housed in tents and fed by the RAF with the initial work being completed in just weeks.

One new arrival in February 1942 remembered his first (aerial) view of three runways in the middle of endless mud and what looked like yellow ants. These, upon closer inspection, proved to be scores of items of building machinery from Wimpey, (known as the Wimpey travelling road show), constructing the airfield and buildings.

A 'Friends of Croome' online newsletter dealt with a recollection from Francis Bird which was taken during the course of their 'Oral Memories' project.

Francis Bird helped to build the runways at Defford. At the age of fourteen years he started work at the airfield and was picked up by a lady driver from 'The Bluebell'. He was taught to drive a tractor with a trailer. The runways were dug out and filled with rubble from Malvern quarries before they were concreted.

Steamrollers flattened the stone and concrete was poured between steel screens. They took their meals in satchels and every morning a little blue Austin Seven van came round with 'lardy cakes' from the Upton Bakery.

In the afternoon a man from the pub at Severn Trent used to bring tea. The adults took their tractors to a hedge near 'The Monkey House', which served strong cider, and had their dinner there. It took two years to finish the runways and dispersal points completely. One week Francis worked ninety-six hours and got £12.10 shillings for his efforts.

* * *

By the 30 May 1942 the TRE staff had fully transferred from Hurn, and priority projects were already operating at 70% efficiency levels. Some of the staff lived at Defford whilst others commuted on a daily basis from Malvern, or were bussed in.

Stella Budden, a mathematician, was one of a small number of female scientists at the TRE. She worked on the mathematical modelling of polar diagrams for radio aerials and flew from Defford on some of the trials.

The move of the Telecommunications Flying Unit (TFU) to Defford was also achieved ahead of schedule, between 24 and 26 May 1942, at which point the station hosted up to seventy aircraft.

Everyone working at Defford was sworn to secrecy and no cameras, public conversations or diaries were allowed. The staff knew the work was linked to radar but not what that actually was. They seem to have held the 'boffins' in awe, and followed instructions to fit numerous items of strange apparatus to aircraft in whatever positions the scientists directed.

Planes would arrive, sleek and aerodynamic, but by the time they had sojourned at Defford for a period they sprouted all manner of aerials, lumps and bumps, from fuselage, nose, wings and tails.

The Canadians are coming – mud everywhere

On 4 October 1940, Sir Gerald Campbell, the UK High Commissioner to Canada, advised the Canadian Department of External Affairs that the RAF was in urgent need of recruits to maintain and operate RDF equipment, as there was a serious shortage of trained radio officers and radio mechanics in the UK.

As a consequence Royal Canadian Air Force recruiting-centres were authorized that month to recruit immediately up to one hundred radio officers, and one thousand radio mechanics.

All possible sources of recruiting were explored, including a broadcast by the Canadian Broadcasting Corporation.

Some six thousand RCAF radar personnel would eventually see service on loan to the RAF and on occasions up to 20% of mechanics on some stations were Canadian.

A number of Canadian personnel also worked on H2S – the 'blind-bombing system' known popularly as the *'magic eye'*, as well as many other systems carried in aircraft.

Canadian aircrew also operated the 'flying end' of radar in fighters and bombers, and many of them tragically paid the ultimate price whilst engaged on this critical area of work. A number are buried in Worcestershire.

Frequently, Canadians formed as much as half the strength of the mechanics on mobile radar units, conducting field training in England before embarking for postings abroad.

Canadians participated in radar research at Malvern helping to devise a number of prototype models of brand new radar systems and flying with them on extensive tests.

* * *

One Canadian, Horace 'Red' Macauley, recollects in *'Canadians at Defford'*, a chapter in *'Canadians on Radar 1940-45'*, arriving for work at TFU in Dorset on 20 March 1942, and being advised to go back and pick up his belongings in Christchurch, before returning to the workshop by 1pm. Such was the level of secrecy that he was told only to mention to his landlady that he was being moved and that he would be in touch later.

The workshop was dismantled and packed for transportation and that evening everything, including all the radar personnel, were loaded onto Lorries and moved to the local rail station, where everything, and everybody, was transferred to a troop-train.

At about 5am the next morning, they arrived at RAF Defford, which was to be the TFU's new location for continued support to TRE who were also on the move to Malvern.

Horace Macauley and his colleagues were not initially impressed with their new home at Defford.

The base was still under construction and the spring rains resulted in mud everywhere. For the first few weeks they lived in their Wellington rubber boots, and only took them off to enter their sleeping quarters – which consisted of a row of bell-tents.

In those early days they had no floor-boards under the tents and made make-shift duck-boards to lift their bedding a couple of inches off the damp ground.

As the weather improved and construction moved closer to completion, the personnel were moved into Nissen huts and matters improved as the newcomers were able to take in the natural beauty of their surroundings and explore Pershore and Evesham, as well as the City of Worcester on their days off, using the obligatory bicycle for transport.

The Canadians also remember the local 'Cider Houses', such as 'The Monkey House'.

> 'Everyone was aware of the power within the rough cider that many farmers had for sale at a going price of 8d (old pence) per pint. The guideline was; one pint and you rode the bike with caution; two pints and you walked the bike home; three pints and you went back for the bike in the morning.'

By late spring the radar section of which Macauley was a member had seventeen technicians – one American, 'Yank' Allan, six Canadians, and ten RAF personnel.

Whilst the majority of their work involved daily inspections and the servicing of Mk 4 and Mk 5 AI, (Airborne Interception), and IFF, (Identification Friend or Foe), equipment fitted in Blenheim, Halifax, Anson and Beaufighter aircraft, they were occasionally called upon to work on other aircraft used for transport, and experimental fitments which included the Hurricane, Wellington, Lysander and Oxford aircraft.

By this time, the 'long-nosed' Beaufighter fitted with the Mk 8 AI radar was a common sight, and a curiosity to those not familiar with 10 centimetre radar, (see Chapter 2).

Mk 6 AI radar was installed in a Hurricane, but never went into production due to the pilot's difficult task of watching the tube and also searching in the darkness for the enemy.

Other Canadian RDF mechanics were employed on the station, such as John McDonald, from Ottawa, who was with the 'Offensive Section' at Defford for nearly three and a half years. During that time he worked on radar equipment in well over thirty-five different aircraft types from Bomber, Coastal, Fighter and Transport Commands.

The scope of radar equipment increased considerably as new systems were developed to assist aircraft in navigation, bomb aiming, gun laying and support to the bomber stream by specially equipped fighter aircraft. Some of the systems included ASV (air to surface vessel), H2S (navigational aid and blind bombing device), AGLT (airborne gun laying in turrets), GEE (navigation system), LORAN (long range navigation system), GEE-H (blind bombing and precision navigation), OBOE (blind-bombing system), IFF (identification friend or foe) and various types of Airborne Interrogators and Transponders (the chapters on radar cover these systems in more detail).

Another group of Canadian radar personnel were employed in the Special Installation Unit at RAF Defford.

Boeing 247-D

This is the unique story of just one of the planes that made its way to Defford.

When the Boeing 247 first flew in 1933 it was at the forefront of airliner technology.

During the 1930s Boeing 247-D – NC1 3344 flew various routes across the United States.

At one stage the aircraft was sold in an 'arms-deal' to the Republican side of the Spanish Civil war, but at the last minute a US Government arms embargo prevented its shipment.

By 1940 the plane had been superseded by newer airliners and this particular Boeing was sold to Canada on the 10 August 1940. They desperately needed military training aircraft and it then served as RCAF 7655.

The Tizard Mission (see Chapter One), led to a partnership with the USA and Canada in numerous scientific fields, one of the products of which was to eventually give this particular Boeing a place in aviation history, after Canada offered it to the British.

The Boeing was chosen as a demonstrator for the American prototype 10cm air intercept radar, (See Chapter 2), and the plane was sent to Britain in July 1941, where it became DZ 203 with the RAF.

The plane arrived at Liverpool on the 27 July 1941 and by the 2 August 1941 had been re-assembled.

One of the first people to fly the Boeing in Britain, and ultimately one of the last, was the then Flight Lieutenant Frank Griffiths who test-flew it on the 2 August 1941.

Boeing 247-D moved to Defford from Hurn with the Telecommunications Flying Unit on 23 May 1942 and was described as a *flying test-bench*.

The plane had a large cabin for equipment and technicians, and side-by-side seating for the pilot and either an observer or radar operator. The baggage compartment in the nose, with a hinged nose-cone opening, as an access hatch, gave space for a circular parabolic dish mounted on the scanner of the American 10cm radar.

The American and British equipment was set up to cater for comparative testing and whilst the American equipment had more power, the British set could pick up signals that were much fainter.

The British receiver was connected to the American scanner and it was immediately found that the system could pick up a target that was three times further away than previously thought possible.

* * *

After proving the US radar, which was developed to equip the RAF's 'night fighter' squadrons, the Boeing was chosen to carry out the first flying trials of the revolutionary 'X-Band' 3cm Radar.

X Band radar was installed in the Boeing and design problems resolved. A magnetron for the new wavelength had been developed and transmission and receiver systems defined.

Whilst this work was underway Frank Griffiths made a number of flights in the Boeing.

In May 1942 the structure of the TFU at Defford consisted of three sections namely – Defensive, Offensive and Naval.

The Boeing was initially allocated to 'B' Flight of the Offensive Section of which Squadron Leader Frank Griffiths was the Officer Commanding.

On the 10 July 1942 a notice was issued by the Ministry of Aircraft Production (MAP) ordering that, for the purpose of the

X-Band trials, the plane would be placed in the *'Top Secret'* category.

Being afforded *'Top Secret'* status meant that it was marked DZ 203/G, between 1942 and 1943, and had to be under armed guard at all times when on the ground.

It was used extensively for the 3cm radar trials between July and October.

On 3 October 1942, Sir Archibald Sinclair, Secretary of State for Air, visited Defford for a demonstration which included the 3cm radar in the Boeing.

By then more hangers had been built at RAF Defford and the Boeing was normally housed in one of those.

In November 1942, DZ 203/G was used for trials of a homing system using a transponder beacon.

Mr. J Banner, a TRE Experimental Officer based at Defford, was in charge of this project working closely with Lt. Cdr. A.E. Milward who by then had taken over as the Commanding Officer of the Naval Section.

The Boeing continued to make regular experimental flights, and records show that in 1943 it was still completing work on behalf of the Naval Section, despite its age.

On 19 September 1943 however, it was decided that the Boeing had no further usefulness for radar research and it was stripped of its *'Top Secret'* status the following day. At that point it was earmarked for transfer to the TFU Communications Flight – however the plane was subsequently reprieved.

* * *

Frank Griffiths started World War Two as a Pilot Officer but by the end of the war he was a Group Captain and an increasingly influential figure in the field of airborne radar.

He was a remarkable man, like so many from his generation.

On 14/15 August 1943, whilst flying for another squadron, his plane crashed near Annecy, close to the Swiss border. He evaded capture and after several exploits made it safely back home to England where he was subsequently made the Officer Commanding Flying at Defford in January 1944, and served as a Wing Commander.

At this point he was reporting to Group Captain McDonald and was fully involved in trials with various planes.

* * *

One of the new projects emerging was the development of 'Automatic Landing' using a system linked to the autopilot. Once again the Boeing 247-D was identified, despite its age, as being the ideal demonstrator for this purpose. The plane needed an overhaul and new engines, and at one stage was nearly sent to America for repairs, but in July 1944 this course of action was cancelled and the work was carried out at Defford over a three-month period, using up to eight hundred man-hours to complete the task.

On 16 January 1945, after being rebuilt and fitted with new radar at Defford, the Boeing achieved the world's first *Automatic Orbit, Approach and Blind Landing'* at Defford airfield.

The plane was flown by Wing Commander Frank Griffiths with Flight Lieutenant Stewart as his co-pilot and with members of the *'Auto Approach Panel'* on board.

From a fifty-mile range, the aircraft orbited the airfield, and was then lined-up and landed using an auto-approach system called a *'radar localiser'* system and what was known as the SCS-51 glide path.

Amongst many others Frank Griffiths was a key player in both promoting the benefits of the project and flying the plane itself.

His RAF flying logbooks indicate that during his career he flew no less than sixty-seven different aircraft types.

After the success of the world's first 'automatic' landing in daylight, Frank Griffiths was keen to repeat the success of the experiment in fog, and during the hours of darkness, the latter being achieved on the 21 January 1945.

In April 1945 the Boeing was undergoing another trial when the undercarriage jammed as it was coming in to land. A successful emergency landing took place and relatively minor damage that took place was repaired.

* * *

For nearly two years the plane then continued to be used in trials in relation to automatic landing, leading the way for this technology to be adapted for use in the civil aviation industry and to allow airliners to operate in all weathers and darkness – now routine on today's modern flights.

Boeing DZ 203 was finally withdrawn from service in late 1946.

On the 30 October 1946, a meeting of the Aircraft Establishment Committee at Defford confirmed a planned reduction in planes from sixteen four-engine, forty twin-engine, and eleven single-engine aircraft, to ten, twenty, and ten planes respectively.

These figures included the disposal of the Boeing.

John McDonald retired at almost the same time, on the 11 November 1946, and was succeeded by Group Captain D.R. Evans CBE DFC as Station Commander at Defford.

Records show that Captain John McDonald piloted DZ 203 on sixty-three occasions with a total flying time of fifty-eight hours.

Wing Commander Griffiths had forty-nine flights and forty-seven flying hours in the plane during 1944 and 1945 alone.

He flew his last flight in the plane in November 1945.

In July 1947, the plane was finally scrapped after playing a key role in no less than three significant scientific contributions to the war efforts, namely the development of the American 10cm radar used to detect enemy aircraft, the demonstration of the 3cm radar X-Band used for the detection of U-Boat schnorkels, and the Auto Landing System.

Whilst something of a sad ending, the memories of the plane's achievements have lived on and are comprehensively recorded in 'Top Secret Boeing' by Bob Shaw, a member of Defford Airfield Heritage Group.

RAF Defford

In 1942, the Telecommunications Flying Unit immediately began testing radar equipment such as AI jamming, Blind Firing with AI, AI Blind Approach Beacons, Infra-Red Identification Systems, Windscreen Projection and Artificial Horizon, Monica, Beacon Homing, Rebecca, Blind Bombing, ASV (Air to Surface Vessel), various AI versions, Oboe, and the Moonshine project.

Many of these projects are described in more detail in the radar sections of this book.

* * *

In 1942, Defford became an RAF station in its own right, transferring from No 6 Group Bomber Command to No 10 Fighter Command. The Station Commander at that time was Group Captain PJR King, who was also the Officer Commanding TFU.

During 1942, a Royal Naval Section, (RNS), was formed at Defford. They originated from a unit testing ASV, (Air to Surface Vessel radar), in naval aircraft, which was predominantly for use in anti U-Boat searches.

The perilous state of the Battle of the Atlantic meant that being able to find German U-Boats was a priority at that time, (see Chapter Two), and there was a lack of TRE resources to engage in this work.

The RNS section commander was Lt Commander A.H. Milward and he introduced Women's Royal Naval Service staff, (WRNS), who started working in the laboratories, and conducting flight testing of airborne radar devices. This was a contentious issue at the time, as women started to take on more important roles, because it meant that some of the men had to take turns as passengers in the gunner's cockpit whilst their female colleagues did the testing.

These were groundbreaking years for women, who began to take on more and more critical roles across a whole spectrum of activities to support the war effort.

* * *

On 29 June 1942, Wellington Z 805 suffered engine failure on take-off and crashed on the top of the ridge separating the airfield from Croome Court, slithered on its belly down the other side and almost crashed into Croome Court itself, with one engine on fire.

The aircrew bailed out of the plane but suddenly realised that the 'boffin' who had been on-board was not with them. As the aircraft itself caught fire they rushed back only to find him emerging clutching his 'breadboard', (literally a piece of wood bearing electronic test apparatus), to his chest. The scientist clearly felt that his equipment was more important than his own life!

* * *

There were nearly three thousand personnel based at RAF Defford at its height during World War Two, of whom some seven hundred were women. These included members of the WAAF, 'Wrens' from the Royal Navy, ATS members, women scientists, and others working in key roles. Whilst the women of the WAAF did not fly as aircrew, the women of the Royal Navy did, and flew on flying trials from Defford over the Irish Sea and the Atlantic.

The Women's Auxiliary Air Force was founded in June 1939 shortly before the start of World War Two. Initially most of those who joined were volunteers aged seventeen and a half to forty-three years of age. Conscription was introduced in 1941 for single women and childless widows aged twenty to thirty years. Their pay rates were two-thirds of a man's doing the same role.

Mrs Doreen Boller (formerly WAAF Wilson) was posted to RAF Defford in 1943 to become the secretary to the Senior Medical Officer. At some stage she had an accident on her pedal cycle and received injuries to her face and leg.

In normal circumstances she should have gone to the RAF hospital in Evesham for treatment but the SMO insisted that she stay in the Station Sick Quarters at Defford, and a screen was put around her bed so that she could continue to provide shorthand for him.

* * *

During the early part of World War Two, locally obtained dogs were used to guard RAF establishments but in 1942 the Ministry of Aircraft Production Guard Dog School (MAPGDS) was formed. This resulted in professionally trained dog handlers being deployed across the country, freeing up hundreds of men for war duties who had previously been employed as guards.

The favoured dogs were German Shepherds, more commonly known as Alsatians in those days, possibly in part due to a desire not to refer to anything with the word 'German' in it. In the 1940s, dogs were deployed at RAF Defford and in 1946, the year that the RAF Police Dog Training School was established; at least four dogs were still deployed at Defford.

In addition to the 'official' dogs on duty at Defford it also became home for a number of 'waifs and strays' who found their way to the Station Sick Quarters where these dogs were treated with love and care, before moving on. At times it was said, the dogs outnumbered the humans in the hospital, particularly just after the war.

* * *

The Special Installation Unit, (SIU), was set up in October 1942 to fit aircraft from operational squadrons with pre-production radar equipment manufactured by the TRE at Malvern. The SIU was part of RAF Defford but separate from TFU.

The RAF controlled aircraft operations and engineering at Defford, but the experimental radar installations were designed and built by the scientists.

As one might expect, the uniqueness of the work led to 'nick-names' emerging for parts of the installation work with, for example, the outside under-slung radar covering on bombers, the 'radome', becoming known as the *'baby's bottom'*.

* * *

During 1942 and 1943, the airfield build-up intensified with three runways, one of 2,000 yards length, and two of 1,430 yards being built. More large *'Type T2'* hangers were added, two to the west of the main runway, next to the Technical area and TRE site. A third

Fig 6 Radome 'baby's bottom' on Lancaster

was on the south-west side with the Servicing Wing, with another in the south. A further hanger in the north of the site was used for military transport vehicles. The cube-shaped Control Tower was situated near to the main runway.

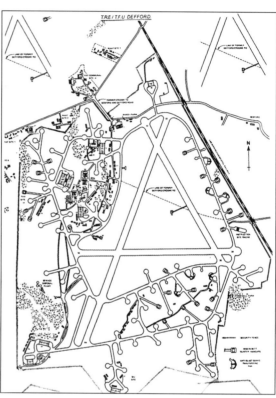

Fig 7 Defford Control Tower from an original photograph

(Right) **Fig 8** Defford circa 1943 showing runways, 'frying pans' and buildings

On the west side, next to the TRE, was the Royal Naval Section, including Naval HQ, washrooms, toilets and laboratories, *'Blister'*, arched portable hangers and hard-standing. Nearby was accommodation for dog handlers.

The airfield was peppered with buildings containing functions such as offices, accommodation, *'ablutions'*, stores, servicing facilities, pillboxes, laboratories, a total of twenty-one *'Blister'* hangars, six aircraft pens, and numerous types of aircraft standings including fifty large *'Frying Pan'* hard-standings.

There were three entrances. The main one was on the north side, with another on the south-west side and a minor one that tunnelled under the railway line from the direction of Defford village and bore gates.

Around the airfield were numerous satellite, or *'dispersed'* sites that provided crucial facilities for what, by now, was a community the size of a large village. There were two self-contained WAAF sites, plus RAF communal sites with a NAAFI, the Officers Mess, a church, showers, washrooms, gymnasium, barbers, tailors, and cobblers shops. By the *'Marble Arch'* (actually the London Arch), at Croome stood further RAF sites containing similar functions plus a cinema and theatre.

Further along the road towards High Green, lay the Sick Quarters with eighteen beds, the Ambulance Station, Garage, Mortuary, Sergeants and Orderlies Quarters and a Picket Post. (Now the site of the Croome Court National Trust entrance, restaurant and the Defford Airfield museum).

When the RAF base was installed at Defford, local enterprises sprang up to service the needs of personnel. For example a 'fruit and vegetable stall' was set up by a Mr Spence outside the walled garden at Croome and he supplied the Officers Mess.

❋ ❋ ❋

Roger Allard was born in 1943 at *'Tower Farm'*, which was part of the Croome Estate.

His mother came from Birmingham and was employed as a district nurse by the Parish. She had a phone in the shed outside the house – somewhat unusual in those days. His father came from nearby Stoulton and at one stage was delivering milk around Pershore, on a horse and cart, on behalf of Captain Bomford from *'Alsborough Farm'*.

In the late 1930s his father took over the tenancy of *'Tower Farm'* which was just a quarter of a mile from RAF Defford.

Roger was three years old when the war finished and as such his childhood memories of RAF Defford are limited albeit the impact of living so close to the airfield has remained with him, and his family, for the rest of his life.

Roger recalls,

'A lad called Dennis was a lodger staying with us at the farm. He was a Canadian airman based at Defford. He was a young man, in his twenties, and never talked about the war. As I look back it never ceases to amaze me how young they all were and the sheer scale of what they were taking on.

I always remember that every time a plane took off the whole of our house shook violently and my mother used to run to the shelves to take the crockery and plates off, as they would literally shake so much that everything would fall off otherwise.

It was mainly Wellingtons and Halifax's taking off then but later we started to see Meteors taking off.

My wife Valerie also comes from the area and her father George Pitman was a farmer who worked at "Blackmore Park Farm" in Malvern.

They had three Land Army girls working on the farm, one from Liverpool called Jenny, and another called Marjorie from Solihull, who got married and stayed there. A lot of the Land Army girls married local farmers.

They had to teach the girls such things as how to milk a cow by hand with a bucket to catch the milk underneath.

George was not allowed to join-up because he was a farmer but he was a member of the Home Guard.

RAF Defford was operational for bombing raids and the aircrew were incredibly brave. I remember one Wellington crashed nearby after two planes collided. The rear gun turret was ripped off and fell into the fields. Whilst ploughing over the years I have frequently come across .303 bullets and pieces of webbing in the soil.

We had another piece of land at the back of the airfield, to the west of it. There was just a wood between it and the airfield and was part of Dunstall Farm. It is an area where as a child I found lots of things like buckles and musket balls from the Civil War.'

* * *

In March 1943, four American radio mechanics and two officers arrived at the TRE in Defford in order to learn more about the ongoing work there.

* * *

LACW, (Leading Aircraft Woman), Beryl Meakin, served in the WAAF between 1942 and 1946 and was at RAF Defford from February 1943 to 1944.

Beryl wrote a number of letters to members of her family during this period, now preserved in the Archives and Library Section of the RAF Museum in Hendon.

The following partial transcripts of one of those letters, dated 29 June 1943, which was written to her parents, provide an intriguing insight into life on the base at the time.

The letter details a meeting with her older sister Joan who went by train to Pershore to visit Beryl, where they had dinner before going for a walk through Pershore:

> 'Joan told me about the Bournemouth raid. The WAAF Sergeants were very brave weren't they? They haven't finished building Defford yet but they say when it is finished the Germans will come and bomb it, as they have watched every move the unit has made from Christchurch, to Hurn, and from Hurn to Defford. Each time the unit has moved because they have been bombed.'

She went on to describe events next day,

> 'After breakfast we cycled to camp......Joan quite liked the WAAF site though she said the hut wasn't as she had imagined it. I showed her S.H.Q. Signals where I work and then we cycled across the aerodrome on the perimeter track. We went through two gates and Joan wasn't stopped or asked for her identity card which was rather amazing. I think Joan liked the aerodrome with all the different kinds of planes.
>
> They were using 5 runway so we could see the planes landing and taking off quite close to us. The four engine bombers were the ones she hadn't seen much before and we saw a Liberator and some Lancasters and Flying Fortresses.
>
> Yesterday we had a 60' flagpole erected outside S.H.Q and next Saturday we are going to have the T.F.U. badge presented to us. I suppose this signifies that Defford is nearly

completed now. We shall have the hoisting of the colours every morning now.

S/Ldr Shaw has volunteered for the "mobile ops room" and will be posted from here very soon. He is dying to do something active and I think this is his chance. It is a very dangerous job and those going out are lucky to come back and if they do there will be "bags of celebrations". Diggy wants to go with Shaw so he is remustering to R.T.O. and hoping he will be able to go with him in that trade. If there is a 2nd front there won't be any mobile ops rooms so they will have had it. Do you know what type of vessel they use for the mobile ops room Daddy? Diggy says they are larger vessels than destroyers.'

In some of her other letters, written whilst at RAF Defford, Beryl also described her duties working as a traffic clerk and mentioned how she was allowed to wear slacks when on duty at night. She described engaging in training exercises, a Morse aptitude test and the possibility of undertaking a wireless operator course at Blackpool.

* * *

The 'disc marking' of the Telecommunications Flying Unit, which was later renamed the Radar Research Flying Unit (RRFU), was displayed on the tail fins of planes engaged in this type of work.

On 3 July 1943, a cast shield depicting the TFU badge was presented by Air Vice Marshall Steel DFC, AOC, (Air Officer Commanding), of 10 Group, at a parade at RAF Defford. During his speech the AOC outlined the history and objectives of the TFU.

The crest is an eagle displayed in gold with a light blue tongue, and inverted wings holding in each claw a red bolt of lightning.

The Unit motto 'FIDE ET FORTITUDINE' translates as 'Faith and Fortitude' – Faith in Radar and Fortitude in experimental flying.

The shield used to hang in the office of Group Captain J.A. McDonald CBE AFC who later that year became the Officer Commanding Telecommunications Flying Unit, RAF Defford.

At some stage, believed to be in the 1980s, a blazer badge was created for the Radar Research Squadron of the RAF who adopted the same motto, which depicted the former TFU emblem.

Group Captain J.A McDonald was the Commanding Officer at RAF Defford between 2 October 1943 and October 1946. He was known as 'Mac' and joined HQ Communications Flight in Northolt as a pilot in 1921 before seeing operational service in Turkey and Shangai.

After a spell in India he was posted, on the 18 September 1943, to Defford.

On arrival he found that morale was low due to a number of fatal crashes which had occurred during the course of experimental test flying of radar equipment. He was a natural leader and flew a number of different planes whilst at Defford, including one from which he was subsequently forced to bail out.

Amongst other things he championed work on the Automatic Blind Landing System.

Group Captain McDonald lived in the Commanding Officer's house in the grounds of Croome with his wife, and five-year-old son Michael, who made friends with a German Prisoner-of-War whose job it was to cut the grass outside with a scythe.

The family immersed themselves in the life of the Defford community and attended events such as the annual Defford Sports Days.

The grounds of Croome provided ideal open space for various sporting events at RAF Defford, and the Defford Airfield Heritage Group have photographs on display in their museum at Croome detailing some of those activities.

In the 1940s, Sports Day events included such things as sprint competitions, tug-of-war, and even a 'knobbly-knees' competition which was judged by the officers' wives. The base also had its own rugby team in 1945.

(*Postscript:* – Group Captain McDonald died in 1983; aged eighty-five years, but his son Michael has remained a strong advocate of Defford, and the work of the DAHG in preserving its history.

In September 1988 Michael presented the TFU shield to the RAF Reunion Association.)

* * *

The camp had its own social-life and Communal Site B, near the London Arch, was the social heart of RAF Defford. It hosted the cinema and NAAFI building, as well as a squash court for officers.

There were groups such as *'The Gremlins'* and *'The Blue Dots'* dance-bands, and a theatre group, as well as appearances by touring concert parties from the Entertainments National Service Association (ENSA), and Army dances.

Local pubs were within cycling distance and evening transport to Worcester was sometimes laid on where the *'Oyster Bar'* was popular. *'The Red Shield Club'* was run by the Salvation Army, hosting various hobbies, including needlework.

Events were subject to approval by the Station Commander.

An example evening function was when in 1944 the *'Typhoons'* band presented *'Let's have a party'* in the Station Concert Hall with admissions at one shilling, sixpence and three pence.

On Communal Site A there was a gymnasium just north of the main entrance to the airfield.

* * *

On the 14 February 1944, Sir Stafford Cripps, Minister of Air, visited Defford, and the laboratories, and congratulated everyone on a *'fine performance'*.

* * *

In May 1944, a new Social Centre was opened and children's Christmas parties were big events which continued after the war for children of the TRE and RAF personnel.

* * *

Eric Knowles DFM flew experimental radar trials with the Telecommunications Flying Unit from November 1944 and records show that he flew no less than twenty-seven different types of aircraft. In 1947 he switched to ground duties at Defford as the Chief Air Traffic Controller.

His Pilot's Flying Log Book is retained in the Archives Section of the RAF Museum in Hendon.

Eric lived with his wife, and son then aged four years, in the huts of the Officer's Married Quarters which were adjacent to the WAAF's site. The accommodation was described as being *'cold and primitive'*.

Aircrews were very flexible and expected to be able to fly anything, such as Wellingtons, Lancasters, Halifaxes, Mosquitos, Stirlings, or Oxfords, to name just a few, whether on short or long flights.

The *'boffins'* demands were high. They would book flights in advance but would ask for all sorts of manoeuvres and types of flights, often at very short notice. It was the job of the pilots to facilitate whatever the scientists required. One or two flights a day was the average.

Things did not however always go to plan, as evidenced on one occasion when a Warwick aircraft was allotted to take scientists out over the sea on the South Coast to test radar. At a low level the pilot suddenly heard a loud noise coming from the starboard engine. It was found that one of the scientists had opened a window and put his camera out to take photos. The wind broke the camera-strap and it flew into the engine propeller breaking two or three tips off it. The plane had to fly back on one engine. No doubt there were a few discussions on aircraft safety drill on the way back!

It is clear that the relationships between the aircrew and scientists were very good, with the groups sharing facilities, some even accommodation, and clearly of necessity information. Often the pilots needed to understand what the testing was about in order to help, although the Defford site was regarded as *'watertight'* in terms of security.

Flight Lt Ron Leavers was at Defford between October 1943 and March 1945 and in the book, *'The Endless Sky'*, by Glyn Warren, he commented that although it was one of the most secret RAF establishments, he had never heard any chat about the place, outside of the camp, and that although the place was well-run the atmosphere was light-hearted.

The aircrew were mainly *'tour expired'*, having completed two or three operational tours and thus were very experienced and competent. Many were decorated for heroic actions on bombing raids and other wartime operations.

The loss of Spitfire EN 915

On the 1 February 1945, Spitfire EN 915 of the TFU took off from RAF Defford, flown by the Station Commander Group Captain John McDonald, and bound for St. David's in Pembrokeshire.

En route the control of the rudder was lost and this prevented McDonald from landing at St Athan despite two attempts. He decided to turn back to base but soon realised that the chances of landing were slight, with the lack of directional control leading to the potential for a collision with other aircraft on the ground.

When this became clear he decided to abandon the fighter and climbed to 9,000 feet from where he safely bailed out from the aircraft.

Frank Griffiths, who was 'Wing Commander Flying' at Defford, on that day, recalled the incident in the 'The Endless Sky' by Glyn Warren.

He decided that the only advice he could give was to tell 'Mac' to bale out of the plane, stressing that he had no chance of landing it, and that he should turn 270 degrees in the hope that he might crash the Spitfire in the less populated area of the Black Mountains.

Leaping over the side of an aircraft would be no mean feat, let alone the loss of an aircraft valued at some £20,000 in 1949.

Frank Griffiths advised him to open the hood, then to trim the plane at 130mph, upside down, before undoing his straps, pulling out the intercom plug and falling out on his back.

Then came the final call, 'Ok Griffiths, I've got the hood undone, plug coming out…'

One can only marvel at the expertise in flying displayed by such individuals and the absolute faith that they shared in each other.

Group Captain McDonald landed in a very muddy field near to the Smiths Instrument factory at Bishop Cleeve, and his aircraft crashed at Leigh Court Farm, The Leigh, Tewkesbury, where it embedded itself twenty feet into the ground, with the wings and tail-plane sticking out. These parts were recovered subsequently and the ground smoothed over.

Within twenty-five minutes of being found McDonald was said to have been sitting in his office at Defford in a clean uniform. The cause of the crash was the failure of a rudder which had been fitted the previous day. It was established that a fitter had been taken off working on the plane for something more urgent, before the rudder locking wires had been inserted into the nuts. A different fitter completed the job the next day, but did not notice that the locking wires were not all in position.

(*Postscript:* – During 1986 an archaeological dig identified the site of the crash but at that stage bad weather prevented any significant finds being made. In the 1990s the engine, and most of the front part of the plane, were recovered buried twelve feet under the ground. The Merlin engine is now on display at the Defford Airfield Museum at Croome.)

The end of the war

Flight Officer Enid Hopkins was in charge of the WAAF station at Defford for two years.

The sleeping quarters for the WAAF were very widely dispersed and she had the difficult task of visiting accommodation blocks every night when on duty.

On one occasion she went in a Lancaster to see the bomb damage in Germany, and came back apparently feeling *'rather sorry'* for the Germans.

Fig 9 *Lancaster bomber*

On 14 August 1945, it was announced that Japan had surrendered unconditionally to the Allies, effectively ending World War Two.

On '*VJ*' night the officers had a party on Bredon Hill. A huge bonfire was lit and sausages and kippers on sticks were cooked.

Back in camp some of the other ranks also had bonfires going, in fact one fire on a WAAF site got out of hand and the Fire Brigade had to be called!

At their peak in 1944 there were some three hundred and thirty-eight WAAFs at Defford, but the post-war station saw their numbers reduce considerably.

Memories

As a result of seeing the details of a programme about Croome and Defford in 2014 '*AR*' subsequently commented online,

> 'Defford also had a Fleet Air Arm Section. My father was an Air Frame Fitter and Petty Officer at Defford. My mother was a Wren there and that's how they met. Dad used to go to Birmingham on a motorbike to deliver and collect packages which were something to do with radar. Various civilian "boffins" from Malvern were based at Defford....My mother always used to talk about the kindness of Lady Coventry towards the Wrens at Defford.'

(PF) commented,

> 'My mother Winnie worked at Defford during the war in the stores area.'

(RP) also commented on the programme,

> 'My parents met at Defford during the war and to this day we don't know what my father did except that he was working on radar development. He was from Bournemouth and she from Solihull. She was a tracker at the airfield.'

One of the contributors to the programme, Albert Shorrock, commented,

'Defford was so top-secret no-one knew what another section was doing....We used to go out scrumping and would go out of the camp on our night off. It was a wonderful place.'

* * *

In November 1945 Harry Scott was posted to RAF Defford where he flew trials over the Atlantic evaluating new navigational aids. He was a wartime RAF Squadron Leader and was decorated with the DSO, DFC and Bar.

Whilst with the Pathfinder Force during the war he had joined the newly-formed No 109 Squadron which was equipped with the fast, and high-flying, Mosquito, and he was experienced in the use of 'OBOE' the ground-controlled 'blind-bombing' system developed by the Telecommunications Research Establishment.

The trials he was involved in also took him to North America and the Middle and Far East.

In the summer of 1946 he flew to the Far East to assess the impact of large electrical storms on the performance of navigation and radio aids.

The so-called *'Cloud Collision Warning Trials'* (Operation Nimbus) got underway when Lancaster PA 417 left Defford with four scientists on board.

The plane returned to Defford on the 8 July 1946.

* * *

On the 7 October 1946 Group Captain D R Evans CBE DFC took over command of Defford.

Between 23 and 29 December 1946 RAF Defford was closed, except for key personnel, as part of what was called *'Christmas Grant'*.

The first Defford Open Day post World War Two took place in 1947 with numerous aircraft lined up on display for the public to view.

* * *

Ken Ashenden was an electrician at Defford in 1947/48, and his memories were recalled in an article in a *'Friends of Croome Park'* online newsletter.

His first recollections were of arriving at Defford Railway Station and being taken from there in one of the Air Ministry vehicles to the RAF Station at Croome.

Ken slept in billets fairly close to the London Arch.

Everyone had bicycles supplied by the Air Ministry.

Strict regulations were in place, for example they were required to get up early on a Sunday for church parade.

A number of 'static pools' were built as a reserve fire-fighting source of water where there wouldn't otherwise be any. One was about fifty yards from the Officers Mess and if the weather was right people used to take the opportunity of having a swim in it. Ken was also known to frequent *'The Monkey House'* when off-duty.

* * *

Between 1 and 7 March 1947, Defford suffered very heavy snowfalls with the camp almost cut-off. A Sikorsky helicopter was used to transport people in and out.

On the 15 March 1947, a gale with wind speeds of 40mph struck the airfield and caused some damage. Following the thaw, staff from Defford assisted the local population by dropping inflated bomber dinghys to stranded farmers in the Severn Valley, who were struck by floods.

During the winter months of 1947, large parts of the airfield froze up, and on occasions the base was forced to close as it became too unsafe to fly.

Novel methods were employed to try to melt the runway ice, including on one occasion the use of Meteor jet engines, but it did not work because they could not be directed towards the ground.

The Royal Naval Section came up with a potentially risky option of building a huge *'Bunsen Burner'* powered by a three gallon tank of 87 octane aircraft fuel linked to the office stove by a ¼ inch copper pipe. Apparently the top of the stove and the chimney pipe got red-hot but in those days 'Health and Safety' was less of an issue!

* * *

In April 1947, the last of the WAAFs left Defford, with their duties being taken over by civilians.

Some of the buildings on WAAF Site No 2 were subsequently converted into officer's married quarters.

* * *

Paul Dallimore recalls his father's work at Defford,

'My father Thomas James Dallimore was born in 1923 in St Johns, Worcester. He was known by his family as 'Jim' and later, when he went to work, was known by his work-mates as 'Tom'.

He volunteered to join the RAF in 1940 and was an aircraft electrician. He had no ambition to go further and stayed in the same role throughout his working life. That said, he was very bright and was an expert in completing crossword puzzles, as well as being able to draw. He was also ambidextrous and was able to bowl in cricket with one hand, and catch with the other – also very useful for holding spanners in confined spaces!

He served at different locations, including I think RAF Moreton in the Marsh and at one point also went to Northern Ireland. I believe that at some point that he was working on Air Speed Oxfords.

In the latter part of 1946 he was demobbed and spent

Fig 10 Tom Dallimore on joining the RAF

six months in a factory before then getting a job with the Ministry of Defence as a civilian aircraft electrician in 1947.

At this point he was posted to RAF Defford.

My father got married to Joan Dorothy Smith, who lived around the corner from where he lived, in 1952.

I was born in 1954 at which point we were

Fig 11 Tom Dallimore at Defford after demob, circa 1948

living in Pershore on the Royal Radar Establishment Estate which was near to Pershore Town Centre. It was at the top end of the Abbey Estate where there was accommodation for technical staff and married quarters for RAF personnel.'

'Tom' Dallimore took many unique photographs of his work, some of which we are privileged to reproduce in this book. They are rare snapshots of a secret time and place.

Fig 12
Servicing Handley Page Hastings at Defford

* * *

On 20 July 1948, Air Vice Marshall C.W. Weedon, (Commanding No 41 Group Royal Air Force), conducted the Annual Inspection of the Telecommunications Flying Unit, Defford, and a copy of his report is lodged in the Archives Section at the RAF Museum in Hendon.

Fig 13 *Tom with colleagues at Defford*

Fig 14 *De Havilland DH112 Venom*

Fig 15 De
Havilland
DH112 Venom

Fig 16 De
Havilland
Devons at
Defford

Fig 17 De
Havilland
Venom

Fig 18 Unknown
male and De
Havilland Devon

Fig 19 *Tom Dallimore in Irvin Jacket with Venom*

(Right) **Fig 20** *Tom servicing a Hastings engine*

Fig 21 *Tom in front of De Havilland Devon*

Fig 22 *Tom with Gloster Meteor*

The report confirmed that the unit was functionally controlled by the Ministry of Supply, but was service manned and commanded by Group Captain D.R. Evans CBE, DFC.

On his arrival for the inspection he was met by a 'Guard of Honour' who were inspected and found to be *'excellent'* in terms of arms drill and turn-out.

Air Vice Marshall Weedon then watched a ceremonial parade which was attended by all ranks, other than those required for essential duties, and the Regional Band from No 3 Area, Locking, which played during the inspection and march-past.

He noted that:

> ...'all ranks remained rock steady after the completion of an order and that the drill movements of markers and officers in the supernumerary ranks were excellent.'

During a visit to the domestic accommodation he made special mention in his three-page report of some of the innovations he found,

> 'I noted that a special room equipped with ironing tables and electric irons had been set aside for use of airmen. This is an excellent idea and is no doubt a contributory cause to the pride the airmen took in their turn-out.'

And,

> 'By arrangement with the Clerk of Works several static tanks had been painted and converted into swimming pools at a cost of £4 each. I have no doubt that these will be appreciated when summer weather comes.'

And finally,

> 'The only Fish and Chip Shop at any station in the R.A.F is sited at Defford. This is open from 9.30pm to midnight and is most popular. This idea might well be extended to other R.A.F. units located away from a town.'

He noted that there was no hot water on the N.C.Os site and that the whole of the plumbing and water-borne sanitation on the Officers' site required completion. On the other hand he found the senior N.C.Os bunks *particularly clean and attractive* but felt that their status as a Warrant Officer was hardly in keeping with *'the requirement that he should polish his own floor and clean out his own fire etc.'* He suggested that, *'a small establishment of batmen should be allowed to look after warrant officers' quarters.'*

He even went so far as to check that the 'swill bins' were clean and responded to a complaint from the Naval Section that their *'bulk'*, i.e. food rations, were not on a par with those of the Royal Air Force.

The Air Vice Marshall went on to inspect the unit's piggeries, guardroom, married quarters and educational facilities which had just taken on an ex-Cambridge undergraduate as an Educational Assistant.

His visit concluded with a visit to the technical facilities on site, including a specific facility for repairing bicycles.

Overall he concluded that 'discipline, morale and *"espirit de corps"* were all maintained at an extremely high level'.

* * *

In February 1949 Group Captain A.M. Rogers became the Station Commander at Defford, and it is claimed that one of his early acts was to have all of the half-pint mugs removed from the Mess as he regarded them as being *'sissy'*.

* * *

In 1950 the Defford Aero Club was formed to provide recreational flying for RAF and TRE personnel from Defford and Malvern. The club purchased several dismantled *'government surplus'* Tiger Moths which were rebuilt, and flying instruction for the Private Pilot's Licence was offered to members.

* * *

On Coronation Day, 2 June 1952, the Air Force at Defford hosted a party for local children. That evening the Coronation Parade was watched on a tiny television set in the Officers Mess.

* * *

In 1953, the TRE merged with the Radar Research and Development Establishment (RRDE) to form the Radar Research Establishment (RRE).

RRDE was the successor to ADRDE at North Malvern, and worked mainly on radar systems for anti-aircraft artillery used by the army.

Defford was renamed as the RRE Air Station.

In 1955, the Telecommunications Flying Unit (TFU) was renamed the Radar Research Flying Unit (RRFU).

Defford Fire Service

William Lowe, more commonly known as 'Bill', was born in Malvern in 1929 and has always lived in the area apart from the period when he was in the RAF, between 1947 and 1955, where he worked as an aircraft fitter.

Bill recalls,

'I was in the Air Training Corps at Malvern from the age of fifteen years, and regularly on a Saturday morning two or three of us would cycle in uniform to the airfield at Defford and report to the person in charge at the Control Tower. More often than not we were successful in being able to go up in one of the big planes on a flight that would last for several hours as the aircrew did training exercises.

Not long after leaving the RAF I became a Fireman with the Ministry of Defence and did my initial training at Manston in Kent.

I was then posted to Defford Airfield as part of the fire-crew there. Normally there would be about a dozen of us on duty in the daytime and about five on nights. We had a foam engine, three fire-tenders and a Land Rover and worked from a Fire Station on the airfield which consisted of three or four buildings and some workshops.

There was a Chief Fire Officer who also covered the fire-staff working at Malvern TRE and he worked between the two stations.

Our uniform was a dark blue/black tunic with buttons that we didn't need to shine, with the same colour trousers, and a peaked cap and MOD badge. We also had a fireman's helmet for operational work.

We did lots of fire drills every morning and also had to have tenders on standby at the control tower when flights were taking place, as part of the fire precautions. There were also fire extinguishers in every office on the base that had to be serviced and maintained.

I don't recall any actual fires taking place whilst I was there. There was always very strict security and you never really knew what was going on other than that they were doing experiments in aircraft in conjunction with Malvern TRE. Cameras were forbidden on the site.

Fig 23 Bill Lowe

After a while a vacancy came up at Malvern TRE and I moved there where there was a small contingent of fire-officers with two or three fire-tenders.'

Bill completed thirty-eight years with the MOD Fire Service and retains a love of aircraft to this day.

Winding Down

Defford's days as an airfield were by now coming to an end, as its location in a saucer-shaped depression bounded by a railway line ruled out runway expansion to cater for the needs of the new types of bombers and fighters.

In one instance a ground fire destroyed an Avro Ashton and its H2S Mk 9 trial equipment was transferred to a 'V' bomber, a Vickers Valiant. The 6,000 feet main runway at Defford was unsuitable for the Valiant which then had to be based at Gaydon in Warwickshire for two years.

Pershore airfield was identified to replace Defford. The RAF vacated Pershore in 1954 and it was then refurbished for RRE use, with the runway being extended to 7,500 feet.

In September 1957 the RRE Station moved from Defford to Pershore.

Defford closed officially for flying at this point, although a few unconnected flights did take place, the last of which was in March 1958.

The Officers' Mess on Communal Site B remained in use whilst facilities were prepared at Pershore. The closure of that Mess in January 1960 marked the RAF's final departure from Croome.

* * *

The testing at RAF Defford of experimental radar equipment created by TRE at Malvern, enabled the 'production engineered', operationally viable, radar devices that helped British Bombers to cripple Germany's industrial output, track German U-Boats, and in the latter stages of the war to severely damage German defences on the Atlantic and Channel coasts, prior to the Allied Invasion. Chapter Two recounts these achievements in greater detail.

* * *

Between 1942 and 1957 almost every type of aircraft in use by the RAF, the Fleet Air Arm, and US Air Force featured at Defford Airfield, filled with innovative and world-leading creations.

'Arrested' – the plane-spotter's honeypot

Plane spotting was an attraction for local youngsters who lived close to the airfields at Defford and Pershore.

Peter Clarke, recalls,

> 'During my wanderings in the middle 50s I used to take pictures of the airfield at Defford on my little old Kodak Box Brownie camera. As a kid in 1957 I was 'arrested' by the MOD Police for taking photographs and logging aircraft details.'

Peter was clearly allowed to retain his 'Box Brownie' and the film inside it. We are very fortunate and grateful for his permission to publish for the first time his unique glimpses of Defford in February 1957, just before closure, together with some of his own descriptions.

Fig 24 *Sad end! Built from uncompleted Tudor II, 1951, Radar Bombing Research at Defford with wing bomb pods. Written Off 1955, transferred to RAE Farnborough for structural testing*

Fig 25 *Bristol 170 Freighter Defford 2.2.57 Air Intercept Radar Testing; First flight 1946, broken up at Blackbush*

Fig 26 Bristol 170 Mk.11 Wayfarer Defford 2.2.57 Air Intercept Radar Testing; First flight 1945, scrapped Gatwick 1965

Fig 27 Bristol 170 Mk.11 Wayfarer. RRE Defford 2.2.57 Bristol 170 VR382 to the right; Avro Ashton WB492 Rear Fuselage right foreground

Fig 28 English Canberra WK120 Defford RRE 2.2.57 scrapped at RRE Pershore 1973

Fig 29 Defford 1957

Fig 30 Defford
1957

Fig 31 Defford
1957

Fig 32 Defford
1957

Fig 33 English Electric Canberra WK120 Defford 1957

Fig 34 Defford 1957

Fig 35 Defford 1957

Fig 36 Handley Page Hastings landing

Fig 37 Defford 1957

Fig 38 English Electric Canberra B2 Defford 1957

Fig 39 Defford 1957

Fig 40 Avro Anson preparing for take off, Defford 1957

Fig 41 *English Electric Canberra B2 Defford 2.2.57*

Fig 42 *Defford 1957, probably an Avro Lincoln*

* * *

Roger Allard, local farmer, continues his recollections,

'I went to the last open day at RAF Defford before it stopped being an RAF base I think in about 1957. I was about thirteen years old and remember that my family sat me on the wing of a Meteor to take a photograph.

In 1959 we came to 'Woodmancote Farm' which again is on the outskirts of the airfield, and just next to 'The Monkey House' Cider-House which is still there to this day. Some of the remnants of the perimeter fence can still be found in the fields.

In one corner of the farm there used to be a searchlight pit with a gun-emplacement. It was eventually filled in but over the years I have found all sorts of bits and pieces of bullets and things there.

On one occasion whilst out in the fields I found a Colt automatic pistol, bigger than a .22 but small enough to fit into the palm of your hand. It was all rusted over having been in the soil but I did some research and discovered that this type

Fig 43 US Secret Service Pistol found by Roger Allard

of pistol was carried by the American Secret Service during the war. Just how did it get buried in the middle of a field in Defford with a loaded magazine inside which I managed to remove and dispose of?

Over the years I got to know a man called Norman Graham who was in his 90s when he died recently. He was Scottish and was a civilian working at the airfield, although he lived in Malvern.

He used to come and service our "Tirollia" wood-burner every year and he just loved everything that was technical. He would read up on all sorts of strange things and when we met he would share bits of what he had learnt. On one occasion he presented me with an article on "The origins of artificial insemination in cattle" – he was a real character.

He told me one story about how they were testing radar and as they were coming back into land at Defford they were too low and clipped the top off an apple tree. He was telling the story to one of the locals one day who responded "I know, I was in the tree at the time picking the apples."

In later years Norman said that he had something to do with the development of radar guns used by the police to detect speeding.

At some stage myself and my brother had a contract to demolish some of the runways at Defford after they stopped using it altogether. There was a rumour that somewhere in one of the marsh areas was a complete bulldozer that had sunk into the ground one day and eventually had just been left there with concrete filled in over the top.

We had a rough idea where it might be but never managed to find it. God knows what else is still buried under the ground there.

I am now the longest-serving tenant farmer on the Croome Estate.'

Fig 44 *Roger Allard with surviving Hangars in background*

* * *

Rogers Allard's son Michael was born in 1971 and recalls,

'I spent all my childhood living on the farm to the SSE of the airfield where my parents live to this day on the Pershore to Upton on Severn Road. I have spent many hours in the woods to the west called the "salt baths", where the sewerage works, bomb storage, and slit trenches were, near to the last remaining hangers, (Defford Mill). To the east of a wooded area, at the end and to the right of Blue Bell Lane, just after the railway line, is what I know as the old Battle Headquarters, with slit trenches and shelters, as well as other concrete searchlight pads, slit trenches, dugouts, air-raid shelters and buildings that are scattered in odd locations around the area. There were always stories about the airfield and the people and there was always someone in "The Monkey House" to talk about life there, but the older locals from that time have passed on.'

Still attracting attention

Retired PC Dave Coombe, who was previously based at the police station in Three Springs Road, Pershore, recalls that in 1975 there was an *'invasion'* of *'travellers'* who set up an unlawful encampment with their caravans on the runway at Defford. They were there in large numbers, and the Earl of Coventry, who owned the land, asked for police assistance to remove them.

As the police made attempts to move the *'travellers'* a solicitor, acting on their behalf, demanded proof of the Earl's ownership of the land. This delayed matters but eventually the Earl managed to produce the title deeds and again demanded that the *'travellers'* be moved on. Several neighbouring landowners eventually brought tractors and trucks to the airfield, intending to tow the caravans off the site, but other legal issues were raised which prevented this from happening and it was actually some time before they left.

* * *

Colin Bryan, also a retired police officer recalls,

> 'Most of my mother's family came from Defford and the surrounding villages.
>
> My uncle, long deceased, was in the RAF in the 50s somewhere up north and used to get a lift in a Vampire down to Defford when coming home on leave – a perk of being a steward in the Officers Mess I always assumed.
>
> I remember "The Monkey House" well; it was on the main Upton on Severn to Pershore road, on the edge of Defford airfield, an old thatched house that in my day looked a bit tumbled down with wooden barns around it. I never visited it to partake in its cider maybe because of the stories I heard of what they put in the cider. It was a really rough cider they produced so I was told. People used to say you didn't buy it by the pint you had to cut it off by the length!'

* * *

Simon Young a retired West Mercia Police Officer recalls,

> 'I was born in 1960, and in 1977 joined West Mercia Police as a Cadet before becoming a constable in October 1978. My first posting was to Pershore Police Station, which covered the Defford Airfield Site.

On nights there weren't many places to go, in what was a largely rural area, and I used to regularly pay a visit to the gate-house on the airfield which was manned by at least two fire officers at any one time, who also did security as well as fire prevention. I think that they had one appliance there in case of a fire.

The whole of the airfield had a perimeter fence around it, which still exists to this day, and sometimes when I went there the lights would be switched on, and sometimes it was in complete darkness.

The actual runway had become disused by then but it was still a very secure place.

As it was still MOD property, it was also covered by officers from the Ministry of Defence Police who maintained an office at the South Site in Malvern and did mobile patrols in marked cars around several sites in the area.

There was also a Detective Inspector Ian Reed working from there and I always tried to maintain a good relationship with them as they, the MOD Police, had access to technical kit that we struggled to get at times.

Right next to the perimeter fence at Defford was Croome Court, and the "Society for Krishna Consciousness" had their headquarters there. They were a strange lot really and spent a lot of time painting certain areas of the buildings, whilst totally neglecting other areas. The odd stolen car used to turn up in the grounds, and twice I got called there due to people suffering from the effects of LSD. In one case an individual was covered in blood from the waist down after he had tried to castrate himself with a *Stanley knife!*

Just adjacent to the airfield at Defford was a place called "The Monkey House" which sold cider, brewed locally, from a hatchway. I tried some once but it was like drinking syrup.

In the early eighties I dealt with two sudden deaths in the vicinity of the premises, both of whom were from Birmingham. One had been out fishing for the day near to "The Monkey House" and got so drunk that he collapsed out in the open and died of exposure. The other person had been drinking heavily and whilst fishing fell into the River Avon and drowned.

After RAF Pershore closed, at some point West Mercia Police started to use the hangers, and runways there, for advanced driving courses, which included high-speed reversing. I completed a course there in 1986.'

* * *

The fascinating story of Defford airfield continues in Chapter Four with Radio Astronomy, including the building and use of the radio telescopes, and concludes in Chapter Five which takes the tale of this historic and secret place to the present day.

Chapter Two

Malvern – 'The Invasion of the Boffins'

BY EARLY 1942, the vulnerable coastal positioning of the Telecommunications Research Establishment (TRE) at Swanage, given the sensitive and vital nature of its *'Top Secret'* work, was increasingly generating concerns that it would be either bombed, killing Britain's best radar scientists, or that the Germans could raid the site and capture its secrets.

Ironically, the incident that precipitated the move of TRE to Malvern was one of the most daring and successful British raids of the War.

Even before war broke out, there was opposing opinion in the corridors of power as to whether the Germans had radar. Gradually, the Scientific Intelligence Service built up evidence of various examples, including the codenames for German ground radar, *'Freya'* and *'Wurzburg'*.

An excellent and detailed account of the work of British Scientific Intelligence can be found in, *'Most Secret War',* by R.V Jones.

By the autumn of 1941, Freya installations had been photographed but Wurzburg remained elusive. Then a reconnaissance photograph of two Freya radars near to Le Havre was received and it was noticed that there seemed to be a much smaller object, barely a speck on the photograph, served by a path, further along the cliff near to a large villa by the village of Bruneval.

A further photograph was obtained, taken very skillfully and bravely at 300mph by Tony Hill in a reconnaissance Spitfire. This confirmed the presence of a small radar unit, believed to be a Wurzburg, and the paraboloid dish could clearly be seen on the image.

The Wurzburg was situated on top of a high cliff, but there was a traversable slope leading to a small beach below.

A raid was conceived, code-named *'Operation Biting'*, to bring back part of the radar for TRE, who were very keen to examine it. A seaborne Commando assault was deemed too risky, and so on 27 February 1942, paratroops commanded by Major John Frost, landed in the area.

It was their first ever use in this type of operation.

They captured the villa, killing a number of Germans in the process and then dismantled key parts of the radar unit and carried them down to the beach whilst under constant machine gun fire.

There they were met by a naval landing craft containing TRE radar scientist Donald Priest, apparently chosen for his 'adventurous' character. Two paratroops were killed and six captured, whilst five Germans were killed.

Two Germans were taken prisoner, one of whom was a Wurzburg radar operator. The equipment was taken to TRE at Swanage where it yielded much vital information including the wavelength of operation, which was to prove very useful later.

After the war, captured German reports indicated that they thought it was the best British raid of the war.

'Bruneval' is the first battle-honour inscribed on the drums of the Parachute Regiment.

* * *

By April 1942, rumours of a move for TRE gained currency, as the raid at Bruneval had shown that coastal installations were especially vulnerable to paratroop attack. Then came news that intelligence was suggesting that seventeen train loads of German paratroops and landing troops were on the Cherbourg peninsular, with TRE as the target.

On 2 April 1942, weather conditions were perfect and everyone at TRE was on tenterhooks expecting a raid, but none materialized.

There were also concerns that the enemy had equipment, as did the British, which could detect the sites of ground radar stations and could therefore have pin-pointed Worth Matravers as a location worthy of targeting.

TRE was told that Churchill had ordered that they move from the south coast before the next full moon. A regiment of infantry arrived to protect them, placing barbed wire around the site and preparing to put explosive charges in the most secret equipment. Sporadic air attacks on Swanage occurred and Luftwaffe bombers were constantly passing overhead en route to their city targets.

On 24 April, Lovell noted in his diary that Malvern had risen to the top of the list for TRE location.

This disruption made further work on testing H2S in the Halifax at Hurn airfield very difficult, and on 1 May 1942 an official statement notified that TRE was to move to Malvern Boys College.

It was also decided that the Air Defence Research and Development Establishment (ADRE) should move at the same time, from Christchurch to Pale Manor Farm, Malvern.

This was later known as RRE 'North Site' in Leigh Sinton Road, Malvern, where a workshop was constructed in three months by women of the Emergency Building Corps.

On 25 April, government inspectors had visited the college and the Headmaster H.C.A. Gaunt, had been told by the Ministry of Works, that his school had to move – and it was a War Cabinet decision.

This level of decision-making had been required because the boys had already been evacuated once and had only just returned, accompanied by assurances to the headmaster that there would be no repeat evacuation. It required an order from the highest level in a wartime environment to unseat the teachers and their charges from their school!

Unfortunately, whilst being able to accommodate the TRE, the college was in no way suitable to house the thousand staff and their families who had been ensconced at Swanage in some comfort. In the event the Malvern Winter Gardens were requisitioned to form a vast canteen capable of feeding up to 1,500 people at one sitting.

The scenes at the college were chaotic on the day of the move, as hundreds of staff and their families, and over a hundred Pickford removal vans carrying crates hurriedly stuffed with their belongings, together with entire laboratories worth of equipment, crammed into the area.

It was raining and there was mud everywhere. Squads of builders were erecting buildings on every available patch of ground. The college houses were converted to laboratories and workshops, with internal partitions for the dormitories ripped out and new heating systems installed, with new boilers and brick-built boiler houses. Floors required strengthening with girders and hundreds of miles of electrical cabling had to be laid, including a complete ring main around the playing fields perimeter to power the laboratories, and new living accommodation, together with high capacity electric cables from Gloucester.

Barbed wire completely encircled the College.

Further construction included air-raid shelters, emergency water tanks, blast-proof walls and three new electric power-stations.

For the Photography Unit a studio, film theatre, artists' drawing-office, animation camera rooms, and darkrooms were provided. There was also a 'photostat' room housing a gigantic copy camera, the products of which had to be pegged onto a washing line to dry. Chief Superintendent Rowe's wife, Molly, volunteered to be the Photostat Operator and was very popular.

In six weeks of fevered construction work a very large steel-girdered workshop with 14-inch brick walls was completed, together with numerous huts and other buildings for TRE use.

Accommodation varied greatly.

Young and single males were mainly lodged in College Houses 5 and 9.

The Chief Superintendent, A.P. Rowe, and his wife lived in the top flat in House 9 thus exercising some 'supervision', whilst House 5 had a 'livelier' reputation.

Some of the older staff shared proper bedrooms, but most of the youngsters were billeted in dormitory style quarters that they called 'horse boxes'. These were 6 foot by 6 foot sleeping spaces containing a bed, dressing table, wardrobe and chair, separated by wooden partitions with just a curtain for a door.

One new member of staff, Richard Burberry, reminisces in Colin Latham's book, 'Pioneers of Radar', that,

'My base for five years was a 60 foot wooden-framed, tarred-paper walled hut....alongside a concrete road along the edge of the Aerial Field, the College lower playing field....We had electricity, a cold tap and an outside chemical closet.'

* * *

Geraldine Hostel, part of which now forms Chase School, was built to house industrial workers, and Malvern Girls College, together with The County Hotel, which is now Park View, took in a large number of WRAF personnel.

Retired police officer Derek Hackett has his own memory of Geraldine Hostel,

'As a former member of the Worcestershire Constabulary in the early 1960s I remember that police officers from all over Worcestershire were billeted at the Geraldine Hostel, Malvern, for a week during the Three Counties Agricultural Show.

The Geraldine was a military hostel to accommodate servicemen stationed, or visiting, the radar installation in Malvern.

I was a new recruit and was there for two weeks in June 1963 when I had to furnish the cell-like rooms with beds, mattresses etc. ready for the invasion of hungry and thirsty police officers!

It was not far from the town-centre and similar in design to the old Ryton-on-Dunsmore Police Training Centre and wartime billet blocks that were built.

During the show, myself and two other recruits, were utilised in making tea and sandwiches.

Duties were either inside the showground or on the less preferred job of traffic duty. Officers were accommodated at the hostel for five nights. Obviously a good social time was enjoyed when away from the confines of wives and family, and the beer consumption in Malvern licensed houses was greatly increased.

It was a welcome diversion from the daily policing routine in the county.'

Geraldine Hostel was used after the war to house the scientific staff required to leave Malvern College when the TRE moved to the 'HMS Duke' site – a brick-built Naval training station in St Andrews Road.

From 1948 apprentices were also accommodated there.

* * *

The rapid development of TRE at Malvern continued.

Two shops in the centre of Malvern were turned into a war-worker's club, the 'Piers Plowman', where everyone 'mucked in' to help keep the club running.

A TRE revue company was formed and groups called the 'Zenith Players' and the 'Piers Plowman Players' performed plays. There were also music ensembles and the College gymnasium became a focal point for activities, including Home Guard dances.

The final layout at Malvern College was:

House 1: Administration
House 2: Navigation Aids, Rebecca, Eureka
House 3: Aerials and Receivers
House 4: RAF Liaison
House 5: Hostel
House 6: Post Design Services
House 7 (at The Lees): Electronic Countermeasures
House 8 and Preston Laboratory: Centimetric Devices
House 9: Hostel
School House: Ground Radar
Big School: Trainers for Service Demonstration
Pavilion: Circuit Design
Memorial Library: Drawing Office
Monastery: Lecture School
Rackets Court: Environmental Test Chambers
Gymnasium: Stores

* * *

It is reported that some of the inhabitants of Malvern were shocked at, and hostile to, this invasion.

The town had been little affected by the war up to then, and due to the 'Top Secret' nature of the work, the locals could not be told anything about why they were being so imposed upon. Strangers were forcibly billeted into local homes and hotels, and the locals had to provide a room for five shillings a week, and breakfast for an additional guinea. There were also questions about why so many young males were not in uniform, and apparently escaping the fighting, but of course their identity or work could not be revealed.

Lovell recalled that the canteen effort at the Winter Gardens was incredible. It was staffed by the Women's Voluntary Service and delivered good food, the only downside being the queuing, as 1,000 people were fed at a time.

After the relative comfort of Swanage, conditions were however initially poor, but TRE was there to do a vital wartime job, so people just *'got on with it'*.

In 1942 a new Engineering Unit was built in just eight months, becoming known as *'The Factory'*, on the site of what is now Malvern Hills Science Park.

This was a very impressive building containing a large machine unit with brand new lathes and milling machines, two instrument units, wiring and transformer units, a sheet metal and fitting unit, heat treatment facilities and a tool room. On the first floor was a drawing and design space. Underground shelters provided safety.

In *'Pioneers of Radar'* R.V. *'Polly'* Perkins, machine-shop supervisor, remembered it as,

Fig 45
Engineering Unit
January 1943

Fig 46
Engineering Unit September 1943

Fig 47
Engineering Unit Sept 1943

'A happy shop with the girls and chaps all pulling together and singing songs. It was a treat to hear the whole shop belting out "Onward Christian Soldiers". The girls adapted quickly to the work: many had never seen a lathe before yet they turned out to be damn good machinists.'

Fig 48
Engineering Unit Nov 1943

Fig 49
Engineering Unit Machine Shop 1948

On 19 July 1944, King George VI and Queen Elizabeth visited Malvern and *'The Factory'* and conducted a medal ceremony. During the visit they were presented with an Engineering Unit manufactured, *'memento of radar'*, commemorative item.

Fig 50 George VI visit 19/7/44 Engineering Unit Entrance

Fig 51 George VI visit on 19/7/44. Inside Engineering Unit workshop with Mr Betts Foreman and Air Commodore Gregory

'Polly' Perkins stayed at Malvern after the war as head of the mechanical engineering workshops, and instructor of mechanical engineering at the College of Electronics in Malvern.

His last role was Safety Officer at RRE Malvern, before retiring in 1975.

Fig 52 *George VI visit 19/7/44 Radar Memento presentation A.P Rowe Superintendent RRE & Air Commodore Gregory*

* * *

New recruits to TRE at Malvern had to be trained, as radar was *'classified'* and there were no textbooks or learned articles available for general dissemination.

An introductory course was held at Townshend House, a former monastery owned by Malvern College and situated in College Road, Malvern.

The course included a trip to Bawdsey, where trainees climbed the 'Chain Home' transmitter masts.

Disaster Strikes H2S

The embryonic H2S equipment was moved to Malvern from Dorset, and the two TRE Halifax test-bombers from Hurn were transferred to Defford airfield, the new home of the Telecommunications Flying Unit.

By now, the original *'Town Finder'* project, as it was originally known, led by Professor P.I. Dee, was well established, and its success in the early trial over Southampton led to the successor project called 'Blind Navigation', or BN for short.

Bernard Lovell was appointed as the project leader, with EMI being selected for engineering development and production. However, the absolutely critical work of TRE itself on the Plan Position Indicator (PPI) should be recognized, which allowed the display to appear as a true map for the aircraft navigator.

At this time, tests of both the klystron and magnetron were still being continued in parallel, with the klystron unit being now fitted into Halifax R9490 and the experimental magnetron into Halifax V9977.

EMI engineers, led by brilliant scientist Alan Blumlein, were at Defford, engaged in testing and development of the then prioritized klystron unit.

Following initial EMI work on a klystron version, the magnetron-based sets superseded the klystron in March 1942.

The situation as regards the competing units at this time was that the klystron powered unit was still favoured by the Air Ministry, but was privately viewed by Lovell and his group as incapable, even with a power boost recently engineered by the EMI work group, of achieving the range and altitude measurements required.

The magnetron powered H2S unit was however looking promising, as various adjustments and 'tweaks' had led to optimism that it could fulfill the Ministry requirements of detecting aircraft at 15 miles range, and 15,000 feet altitude.

On Saturday 6 and Sunday 7 June, Lovell and his H2S group met with Blumlein and the EMI group at Defford.

When the EMI group returned to their Tewkesbury hotel, on the Saturday evening, Lovell flew in the *'magnetron Halifax'*, and witnessed an impressive performance by the H2S unit.

It was therefore arranged that Blumlein and his two EMI associates, C.O. Browne and F. Blythen, should see a demonstration of the magnetron unit onboard Halifax V9977 on the afternoon of Sunday 7 June 1942.

Lovell was engaged in a meeting so did not go on the flight himself – a commitment that prevented the course of history being changed.

The Handley Page Halifax test aircraft, V9977, left Defford at around 3 pm that afternoon carrying the experimental version of H2S Radar, and eleven occupants – aircrew and scientists.

The object of the flight was to produce photographic images of the ground echoes from the radar as the aircraft flew over the Severn Estuary, the coastline and the towns of Cardiff and Swansea.

It was a glorious summer's day, perfect for flying, with bright sunshine and good visibility, but shortly after 4.20 pm, the plane plummeted into a hillside in a field near to the village of Welsh Bicknor in Herefordshire.

At an altitude of 500 feet the Halifax developed an engine fire that rapidly grew out of control. The aircraft was seen to lose altitude, rolled, inverted, and struck the ground.

Onslow Kirby lived, and worked, on Green Farm on Coppet Hill. He was in one of his paddocks when he heard the roar of a low-flying aircraft coming from the direction of English Bicknor. Suddenly, the Halifax, streaming fire and smoke from its starboard wing, appeared. It was no more than 350 feet above his head, coming straight for him.

The fire was burning through the struts holding the wing in place and as the wing fell off, the plane turned upside down and vertically dived into the ground, exploding and bursting into flame.

The falling wing missed Mr. Kirby by just 250 yards.

The fire was ferocious and there was nothing Mr. Kirby could do to help except to call the fire brigade.

The crash spread aircraft parts over an acre, (0.4 hectares), of land.

The brave men who died were:

Pilots:
First Pilot: Pilot Officer D.J.D. Berrington (115095)
Second Pilot: Flying Officer A.M. Phillips (44185)
Crew:
Observer. Flight Sergeant G. Millar (751019)
Flight Engineer. Leading Aircraftman B.D.C. Dear (571852)
Wireless Operator/Air Gunner. Aircraftman II,
B.C.F. Bicknell (1271272)
Passengers:
Squadron Leader R.J. Sansom (33372) (Attached T.R.E.)
Pilot Officer C.E. Vincent (110285) (Attached T.R.E.)
Mr. G.S. Hensby, Civilian T.R.E.
Mr. A.D. Blumlein, Civilian E.M.I.
Mr. C.O. Browne, Civilian E.M.I.
Mr. F. Blythen, Civilian E.M.I.

The immediate recovery of the highly-secret cavity magnetron device was essential, and a team led by Lovell, driven by Group Captain King, the Station Commander at Defford, arrived at the crash scene that same night.

The magnetron was the only piece of the H2S equipment recognizable.

Lovell recollected his feelings as follows,

> 'I was still a young man in my twenties, accustomed to reading about the slaughter in the war, but not to firsthand acquaintance of colleagues lifeless under sheets near the charred remains of a bomber in which I had flown unconcerned the previous evening......I believed this to be the end of the H2S project. We had lost important members of my small group, the key EMI staff, including the genius of Blumlein.'

Alan Blumlein was indeed a genius, and up until recently remained unknown to the public, due to the *'Top Secret'* nature of his death. His story, and the immense loss his death represented, is worth recounting.

The Man Who Invented 'Stereo'

Alan Dower Blumlein was one of the most prolific and brilliant scientists, engineers and inventors of the Twentieth Century. Yet until recently, hardly anyone had heard of him.

Belated recognition has finally come his way, including the award of a *'Grammy'* in 2017. Anyone interested in the life and work of this towering intellect and true war hero should consult the definitive work on his life, *'The Inventor of Stereo: The Life and Works of Alan Dower Blumlein',* by Robert Alexander.

Alan Blumlein spent the final few months of his life working at Defford, and died on a flight from there in the service of his country.

The H2S radar project was so secret that both his death, and his achievements, became buried under government restrictions for decades after the war, along with the vital and pioneering work conducted at Defford and Malvern.

This secrecy spread across his whole life story and he became 'lost' in history.

Alan Dower Blumlein was born on 29 June 1903 in Hampstead, London. His future career seems to have been determined by the age of seven, when he presented his father with an invoice for repairing the doorbell, signed *'Alan Blumlein, Electrical Engineer'*, with 'paid' scrawled in pencil on the bill.

It is said that he could not read until the age of twelve years, and when asked he confirmed this but added, *'but I knew a hell of a lot of quadratic equations'.*

He became interested in, and almost obsessional about, electronics and mathematics from a young age, and also developed a keen interest in steam locomotives, which added mechanical engineering to his skills.

Of course he did learn to read, in fact so well that within two years of his alleged illiteracy he won two scholarships to both Aldenham and Highgate Grammar Schools.

Blumlein eventually attended Highgate School, at the age of fourteen and a half, choosing it as it had a good reputation for science. He later entered the Science Sixth Form where he stayed until 1921, when he was eighteen years old. He subsequently sat the entrance examinations for City and Guilds College in London, one of the best science establishments in Britain at the time.

Blumlein not only passed, he was put straight into the second year after obtaining a Governor's scholarship.

In June 1923, he qualified as an Associate of the City and Guilds Institute with a First Class Honours in electrical technology, distribution and utilization, electrical machine design and electrical generation – he was just twenty and already excelling.

Blumlein was chosen by Professor Mallett of City and Guilds Institute – who at the time was running a postgraduate course in telephony and wireless telephony.

Whilst working for Mallett, Blumlein met and collaborated with several students who would feature later on with him at Columbia Gramophone Company and then EMI.

Professor Mallett secured Blumlein a post with International Western Electric in 1925, highly recommending him. IWE were involved in telephony development on an international scale and Blumlein was suited to this work, working on interference on telephone lines.

In 1929, Blumlein joined Columbia Graphophone Research Department. Within a short time he produced an advanced 'moving coil wax-cutting machine' for cutting gramophone record masters. He also designed a moving coil microphone.

Around 1930 he became interested in stereophonic recording and reproduction. His work resulted in an outstanding patent on the subject and a new method of cutting stereo disks.

In 1931 the Gramophone Company (HMV) merged with the Columbia Graphophone Company to form Electric and Musical Industries, (EMI).

The majority of Blumlein's inventions came during his time with EMI, and he took out an astonishing 128 patents with them, conducting significant research in both sound recording and television.

That same year, Blumlein invented what he called 'binaural sound', now known as stereophonic sound or simply 'stereo'.

In early 1931, Blumlein and his wife were at a local cinema. The sound reproduction systems of the early *talkies* usually only had a single set of speakers, which created the effect of the actor being on one side of the screen whilst his voice seemed to come from the other.

Blumlein declared to his wife that he had found a way to make the sound follow the actor across the screen.

His patent had the title 'Improvements in and relating to Sound-transmission, Sound-recording and Sound-reproducing Systems', accepted on 14 June 1933 as UK patent number 394,325. The patent covered many ideas in stereo, some of which are still in use today.

Blumlein's binaural experiments began in early 1933, and the first stereo discs were cut later the same year.

In Blumlein's short test films, most notably, 'Trains At Hayes Station', which lasts five minutes and eleven seconds, and 'The Walking & Talking Film', his original intent of having the sound follow the actor was achieved.

EMI was responsible for major research into the design and manufacture of vacuum cathode ray tubes and Blumlein focused upon the engineering of the '405 line' system, being largely responsible for the development of the waveform structure used in the 405-line Marconi-EMI system.

This was developed for the BBC Television Service at Alexandra Palace, the world's first scheduled 'high definition', 240 lines or better, television service.

This work was crowned by the outside televising of the Coronation procession in 1937, linked by an eight-mile long cable to the transmitter. A new type of aerial was required and Blumlein invented the 'resonant slot' aerial.

He became EMI's Senior Engineer by the outbreak of World War Two, resulting in him being transferred directly into war project work, adapting his work in stereo to develop an acoustic direction finder.

In 1939 the Company developed a 60MHz radar patented by Blumlein and E.L.C. White.

Blumlein was involved with a visual display for the stereo sound locators in use for gun laying. By 1940 it was delivering airborne interception radar for Beaufighters.

In 1941, when Lovell was ordered to form a group of scientists to develop the long-range bombing aid H2S, the government turned to EMI and its brilliant electronic engineers to move the system from experimental to operational status.

As Blumlein had already worked on the Airborne Interception 1.5 metre radar for night-fighters, he became closely involved with H2S, developing a system that could project a map of the ground onto a screen inside a flying aircraft. He was mainly responsible for the circuitry, especially for data handling and display.

* * *

The loss of Blumlein at this crucial moment in the war effort was both a tragedy for science and a devastating blow to the H2S project

After the RAF investigative board completed its report on the Halifax crash on 1 July 1942, it was distributed to a restricted list of approved recipients, but not publicly divulged.

In the interests of wartime secrecy, the announcement of Blumlein's death was not made for another three years.

The investigative board found that the crash was caused by engine fire, attributed to the unscrewing of a tappet nut on the starboard outer engine, which had been 'improperly tightened' by an RAF engine fitter while inspecting the engine some three hours prior to the crash.

During the flight, the loosened nut caused increasingly excessive valve clearance eventually allowing collision of the valve head with the rising piston fracturing the valve stem. This then allowed the inlet valve to drop open, resulting in the ignition by the spark plug of the pressurised fuel/air mixture within the inlet manifold and, eventually, the pumping of the ignited fuel along the outside of the engine, leading to an extensive fire in the engine nacelle.

Due to the fire originating in the induction system, where the supercharged fuel/air mixture was at higher pressure than atmospheric, the heart of the fire was much hotter burning and intense than would be the case in a simple fuel fire.

Constantly fuelled by the broken intake, the fire burned rapidly along the wing and fuselage, eventually causing the outboard section of the starboard wing to separate from the centre section at approximately 350 feet of altitude.

With the loss of a substantial part of the starboard wing, all control over level flight was lost, and the plane rolled inverted and struck the ground at approximately 150 mph.

The board found that the crew and passengers had not jumped immediately from the aircraft owing to several factors, including a loss of altitude while attempting to find an emergency field, the rapidly spreading fire, which blocked or impeded egress from the plane, and the fact that a sufficient number of parachutes were either not on board, or were not being worn.

Almost immediately following the crash, Churchill issued a directive requiring any test-flights with civilians or scientific personnel to carry a sufficient number of parachutes for all individuals involved.

Such was the importance of the technology being developed at Malvern and Defford, and so great a blow was this loss, that Churchill ordered the crash be kept 'Top Secret'.

There was no press coverage, not even a mention, and the bereaved families were forbidden to publish obituaries.

The embryonic H2S equipment that was destroyed was crucial to the war effort.

The 'Battle of Britain' had been won, invasion staved off, 'The Blitz' withstood, and Bomber Command had been tasked with carrying the fight to Germany, but the British public did not know that they were at this time struggling to hit their targets with the accuracy required.

It was this shortcoming that H2S was designed to rectify – to enable precision bombing of assets vital to the German war effort.

Once 'Classified', the events of that day, the identities of those who gave their lives for their country, and the projects they led, were never 'Declassified' and subsequently became lost in secret official records and the mists of time.

* * *

Meanwhile, the pressure to deliver a 'production' version of H2S in quantity was mounting. Indeed on the day of the Halifax crash Churchill wrote to the Secretary of State for Air, expressing his deep disturbance at H2S' rate of production and ordering that it be prioritised.

The Halifax crash took the heart out of the H2S project at the time, and it was close to abandonment. But the war continued, and the Allies suffered a major setback with the loss of Tobruk.

Churchill withstood a vote of no confidence in parliament then chaired a meeting on H2S on 3 July, the day after the vote.

The atmosphere was gloomy. Apart from the huge setback in Egypt, the H2S project was at a standstill. There had been no flights for nearly a month. The Magnetron H2S equipment had been destroyed, along with the vital EMI scientists.

Lovell had assumed that the issue of H2S would pale beside the potential loss of Egypt to Rommel, but was surprised to find a high-powered set of attendees at 10 Downing Street, including Sir Archibald Sinclair, the Secretary of State for Air, Colonel Llewellyn, the Minister of Aircraft Production, Shoenberg, the Head of EMI, Robert Watson-Watt, Vice-Controller and Scientific Advisor – Communications Equipment, Sir Arthur Harris, Commander in Chief of Bomber Command and Sir Robert Renwick, Chief of Communications, plus other senior officers and staff.

Churchill chaired the meeting wearing his trademark blue boiler suit, sitting alone on one side of the long table, the others arrayed facing him. He demanded 200 H2S sets by 15 October, but was informed of the impossibility of that request.

It was suggested, not by any of the scientists actually involved, that the unit could be constructed on 'breadboards' – wooden boards used to mount temporary circuits and prototypes.

After two hours Churchill had to leave to chair a Cabinet meeting and ordered the attendees to an adjoining room with instructions to not emerge until they had worked out how to produce 200 H2S units by October.

This was not achievable, but the Prime Minister's directive fuelled a fevered round of visits and meetings, resulting in what Lovell still viewed as an impossible target of 200 units by the end of the year. The pressure did result in a crucial decision being taken however.

On 10 July 1942, a meeting at Defford occurred after which Lovell felt that the case for the Magnetron had won the argument.

He was correct, on 15 July the Secretary of State for Air decided that work on the klystron should stop and that the 200 units should be the magnetron version, much to Lovell's relief.

Work was commenced to devise a way of completely destroying the magnetron unit inside any aircraft crashing in occupied Europe.

The race was now on to make the magnetron H2S work properly, and produce and fit enough manufactured units to equip Bomber Command within a five-month period.

There was a big difference between an experimental set of equipment, attached to a 'breadboard', and a suitably engineered and robust unit capable of mass production and routine use in an operational context, and designing the latter was often as problematical and resource intensive as inventing the former.

This enormous task was boosted by the involvement of two new figures, Air Vice-Marshall Don Bennett, the Commander of the Pathfinder Force of Bomber Command – a newly created target-finding force, and Sir Robert Renwick, a staunch supporter of radar and its potential.

Bennett was seen as the greatest flying expert in Bomber Command, and Renwick had direct access to Churchill, giving him the ability to steamroller through supply obstacles of all kinds.

Renwick reassessed the project and on 24 July 1942, a more realistic schedule of equipping twenty-four Halifax and twenty-four Stirling bombers with magnetron powered H2S by 31 December was issued, albeit as Lovell observed, the scientists were yet to make it work properly.

Two Halifax aircraft at Defford were quickly equipped with magnetron powered H2S prototypes but significant problems in the display on the PPI were experienced when flying at 10,000 feet or above.

There was also continuing opposition to H2S within Bomber Command, with divisions between the new Pathfinder Force, and existing units who maintained that they could navigate precisely to targets without H2S, as evidenced by the 'Dambusters' raid on the Ruhr dams in May 1943.

The Americans were also 'lukewarm' tending towards outright opposition, possibly because they were testing 10cm airborne radar far away from the cloudy skies of Europe and the pressure of war on the UK.

A breakthrough occurred in mid-October 1942 when a test flight at the Bomber Development Unit received positive comments from the navigators using it, especially in terms of its usefulness when flying above thick cloud.

Lovell also conducted a debrief of aircrew returning from a bomber sortie to Cologne, where one after another confessed to not seeing the target at all. This convinced Lovell of the urgent need for H2S despite the opposition.

The project continued, and by the end of 1942, mainly due to delivery from EMI of a batch of production sets of H2S, there were forty-eight H2S equipped aircraft.

The first production H2S Mk 1 sets were delivered to the Bomber Development Unit at Grantham Lodge and, subsequently, to the newly-formed RAF Pathfinder Force, in August 1942.

H2S was first used operationally over Germany on the night of 30-31 January 1943, when six Pathfinders led one hundred Lancasters on a bombing raid on Hamburg in appalling weather.

The reports from the returning crews were enthusiastic. There was no possibility of visual target identification, but H2S identified not only Hamburg and its docks, as bright lights sticking out into the darkness of the Elbe, but various navigation marks such as coastlines, estuaries and rivers en route, at an average range of twenty-three miles.

Two days later, ten H2S Pathfinders marked Cologne for the main bomber force and the following night Hamburg again, followed the next day by Turin.

H2S was a resounding success.

Bomber Command issued a memorandum stating that the system had exceeded expectations in identifying towns and land formations such as coastlines and estuaries in any type of weather.

From a navigator's point of view, H2S produced a fan-shaped beam of waves, narrow horizontally, broad vertically. The aerial rotated once a second causing the narrow band to sweep over ground like the hands of a clock. The PPI incorporated a cathode ray tube which displayed the reflections from ground features as the beam sweep revolved around the screen, meaning that such features glowed on the screen as the beam repeatedly swept over them.

This resulted in, by today's standards, a crude but effective map of the ground that the aircraft navigator could use. Buildings produced much stronger reflections than countryside, sea, lakes and rivers – making cities and large factories stand out.

Fig 53 H2S Dish on a Lancaster

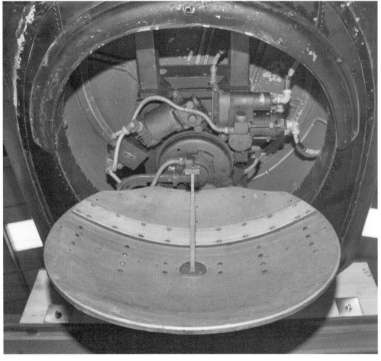

Fig 54 H2S dish showing working parts

H2S identified coastlines, lakes, islands and estuaries even in darkness and cloud. It also enabled aircraft speed over the ground to be measured, and from that wind-speed over the target to be calculated, together with height above ground.

The system still needed some tweaks but the focus now moved to another problem.

H2S and the 'Battle Of The Atlantic'

During 1942 shipping losses to German U-Boat attacks reached 600,000 tons per month.

In the first seven months of the year 681 ships were sunk, supplies of essential materials to Britain were at risk, and the threat posed by U-Boats to the war effort reached a critical point.

U-Boats were able to operate with impunity from French ports in the Bay of Biscay, remaining submerged all day and surfacing to run their diesel engines to recharge their batteries at night.

Whilst the existing ASV 1.5 metre radar was effective in daylight, it was not accurate enough at night. The fitting of a powerful searchlight, the *'Leigh Light'*, beneath Coastal Command Wellington aircraft made an impact, but the Germans then developed a counter-measure known as *'Metox'*. This was a receiver that picked up ASV radar emissions way before Leigh Light range was feasible, allowing the U-Boats to submerge before detection was possible.

The obvious answer was to adapt H2S for submarine detection.

Once more there was debate and obstruction, but the necessary modifications to the H2S equipment were carried out at Malvern College and by the end of February 1943, prototype 10cm H2S ASV units were fitted to a dozen Coastal Command Wellingtons at Chivenor for testing.

This was against a backdrop of disinterest from Coastal Command Officers and annoyance from Bomber Command at the diversion of effort and units from their aircraft and needs.

After a number of test flights without sighting a submarine, on the nights of 17 and 18 March 1943, a U-Boat was detected and on the second night one was sunk. On both occasions the U-Boats were on the surface and therefore unaware of the H2S signal, in other words H2S evaded the *'Metox'* countermeasure.

A further thirteen U-Boat sightings were made by the end of March, and twenty-four in April.

During April and May 1943, fifty-six U-Boats were destroyed and their attacks on shipping ceased towards the end of May.

The small number of H2S equipped Wellingtons completely altered the situation in the North Atlantic to the point that in May every U-Boat traversing the Bay of Biscay suffered at least one attack. Hitler made a radio broadcast in which he blamed the setback to the U-Boat campaign on one technical invention of the enemy.

H2S did not win the *'Battle of The Atlantic'* alone, but it tipped the balance from the jaws of defeat to a slaughter of German U-Boats that continued until the French ports from which they sallied forth to prey on the supply convoys were recaptured after D-Day.

Further versions of ASV were developed at Defford during, and after the war.

ASV Mk XI operated at 3cm and was fitted to Fairey Swordfish and Barracuda aircraft flown from carriers by the Fleet Air Arm.

* * *

H2S was also successfully modified by TRE at Malvern for use in tank landing craft, as an aid to choosing suitable stretches of coastline for *'running onto'*.

By the end of trials on 9 May 1943, the H2S unit was enthusiastically requested, and six landing craft were fitted and almost immediately took part in the Allied landings in Sicily and Italy in July 1943. A year later, the H2S unit was fitted onto tank landing craft for D-Day.

* * *

TRE at Malvern made further modifications to H2S, and conversion kits were fitted to Bomber Command aircraft to rectify problems in the PPI picture at altitudes of 20,000 feet.

Arthur *'Bomber'* Harris had received his instructions to achieve the,

'Progressive destruction and dislocation of the German military, industrial and economic systems, and the under-

> mining of the morale of the German people, to a point where their capacity for resistance is fatally weakened.' *(Directive from the Casablanca Conference 21 Jan 1943)*

The newly converted units were fitted to the Pathfinder bombers by July 1943 and led the main bomber force to Hamburg at the end of July.

This was a crucial test for H2S, as hitherto, OBOE had proved successful in raids on the Ruhr. *'Project Gomorrah'* ran over four nights, 24-25 July and 2-3 August 1943, when up to eight hundred aircraft per night rained bombs upon Hamburg, which lay outside OBOE range. Hamburg was chosen because it was the second-largest city in Germany and its shipyards were the biggest in Europe, housing many U-Boats and ships under construction. It was the most important port in Germany with 3,000 industrial establishments and 5,000 commercial companies engaged in transport and shipping.

Hamburg's location on the coastline rendered it exceptionally vulnerable to precision attack as the H2S equipped bombers could follow the coast on radar and achieve pinpoint accuracy.

The raids were a total success, causing at the time almost unimaginable damage, with 75% of the city, ten square miles, reduced to rubble.

The German High Command was stunned and Albert Speer, Armaments and War Production Minister, concluded that another six attacks of this ferocity upon German cities would cripple German war production and bring about an early end to the war.

On 17-18 August 1943, Peenemunde, on the Baltic coast – the principal German rocket development centre, was largely obliterated by an H2S-equipped force, putting the V1 and V2 programmes back by months.

This attack stemmed from information obtained by a tiny TRE listening station in Worcestershire – as we shall see.

Now a final phase began, the bombing of Berlin.

* * *

Berlin has no distinct outline and is not on a coast. There were few obvious navigation points for bombers to follow.

The H2S picture from the first three nights of bombing raids in August/September 1943 was very confused, and the raids had poor results with heavy aircraft losses.

H2S once again received a battering from its critics, and various solutions, deemed 'crazy' by the H2S scientists, were proposed, including using an OBOE 'repeater' that would need to be designed and produced from scratch in six weeks.

Fortunately, a new, unproven, iteration of H2S was under development, using a considerably shorter wavelength of 3cm, which it was believed would give greater clarity.

A rather desperate, and somewhat unofficial plan was launched by the H2S supporters, including Harris and Renwick, to build six, 3cm H2S sets – called *X-Band*, at Malvern, and have them installed in six Pathfinder Lancasters by the middle of November 1943.

The many existing problems with X-Band prototypes had to be solved in a hurry, and a new shape of scanner was designed, a *'barrel scanner'*, the top-half of which was a barrel and the lower half a paraboloid.

They and the 3cm equipment were fitted into the six Pathfinder Lancasters, tested with promising results at Defford, and delivered on 21 November 1943.

The X-Band Pathfinders were first used over Berlin the next night, when two of the planes reached the target, identified Templehof airport and put down marker flares within one hundred yards of each other for seven hundred and fifty bombers to follow.

Despite some breakdowns in the equipment, a further two raids proved it worked, and a great deal of bomb damage was caused to Berlin.

On the 3 December, Leipzig, another 'out of OBOE range' target, was devastated by one raid led by X Band 3cm H2S.

Goebbels' diary was later quoted as stating,

> 'The English aimed so accurately that one might think spies had pointed their way.'

Meanwhile the United States Air Force, (USAF), had been performing daylight bombing raids over Europe. They had originally had misgivings about H2S but once they were confronted with the clouds and fogs of Europe they had changed their minds and, having heard of the success of 10cm H2S, now wanted it.

The first USAF Flying Fortress arrived at Defford in June 1943. They operated at an altitude of 30,000 feet, and the performance of the system at this height was problematic. Thus the small Malvern team added another developmental burden to their ever-increasing load. By 18 August 1943, tests in Flying Fortresses from Defford began to look promising and on 23 August a large contingent of American aircrew and mechanics appeared at Defford.

TRE and the American staff had to train US aircrew at Malvern, and fit the units to American aircraft at Defford, eventually managing to equip a total of eighteen Fortresses and Liberators.

One H2S radar trainer was a large shallow tank of water with a model of a town and surrounding countryside at the bottom. A quartz crystal on an adjustable mechanism sent out pulses of ultrasonic waves in order to emulate a radar scanner and received returned echoes from the model similar to those that would be seen on the scanner in an airborne bomber.

A group at TRE was formed to design and build training devices for all the radar systems. They created around seventy-five 'synthetic' trainers in five years, used to train approximately 55,000 operators, navigators and controllers who would otherwise have had to take up valuable aircraft and aircrew time – not to mention the perennial risk of crashing!

The first major raid by the USAF using H2S occurred on 27 September 1943, when three hundred Fortresses attacked the port of Emden in thick cloud, led by H2S 'marker' planes, followed by a further, similarly led attack, on 2 October.

The raids caused major damage to the main target areas. After these successes the case for H2S was proven and the USA developed its own version of 3cm H2S called H2X which took over from the initial eighteen planes fitted with 10cm H2S at Defford.

TRE were not involved with the USAF after this time.

* * *

During the early months of 1944, two new versions of H2S were being debated, one an enhancement of 3cm H2S using a larger scanner with computerized navigation and bombing systems, 'X-Band', versus a 1.5cm version known as 'K-Band' or H2S Mk VI.

There was ferocious disagreement and in a typically 'British' compromise, both were progressed.

The devices were built at Malvern and flown and tested from Defford. Eventually at least six different versions of H2S, with various differences, were in existence by 30 June 1944.

Beacons and Transponders

A Transponder, which is short for transmitter-responder, is an electronic device that produces a response to a specific radio signal it receives. A radio beacon marks a fixed location.

Both were used in a number of inventions by TRE in World War Two, and both GEE and OBOE used transponder technology.

Identification Friend or Foe, or 'Parrot'

British bombers returning from missions in Europe had a problem in that German aircraft knew that they could hide within the returning formations to avoid radar detection due to the massed bomber group signals being picked up by British coastal radar stations.

To solve the problem, in 1939 Allied planes were fitted with small transponders which re-broadcast ground radar signals enabling such aircraft to be identified as friendly – the first implementation of an electronic Identification Friend or Foe (IFF).

The signal from the transponder proved to be so powerful that it disrupted ground radar screens so returning pilots would be asked to turn on the transponder at a certain time in order to identify themselves.

The system was known as *'Parrot'* by the British, and the instruction to briefly turn on the transponder was known as *'squawking the parrot'* and turning it off as *'strangling the parrot'*.

Further iterations of IFF were made, increasing its sophistication, and in 1940 TRE produced IFF Mk III, which was the version used for most of the war. Mk III transponders responded to specific interrogators rather than received radar signals. Limited communication was also possible, including the ability to transmit a coded *'Mayday'* response.

The USA used a 'copycat' system so each other's planes could be recognized.

The Germans developed a similar system called FUG 25A that responded to signals from 'Freya' and 'Wurzburg' ground radars.

However the British came up with an IFF transmitter called 'Perfectos' which could trigger a response from FUG 25A and thereby identify any German night-fighters in the area using the system. It was also discovered that an IFF transponder mounted on a tower near an airfield could be used by aircraft returning from sorties and bombing raids to find 'home'.

It is beyond the scope of this book to cover the complete history of the progress of developments of IFF, both until the end of the war and also until the present day. However, suffice to say, that it has been an important area of research, development and operational application for TRE and its successor Establishments.

For several decades, the military Mk10 IFF has been almost a universal standard, with Mk12 being a US development adjunct.

New and technologically advanced military IFF has been researched and its deployment is envisaged.

Civil aerospace developments of IFF, commonly known as Secondary Surveillance Radar (SSR), are now heavily relied upon in civil air traffic control and management.

SSR is used across the globe in aviation as a means by which Air Traffic Controllers can identify all the passenger and freight planes in the air together with their altitude and position.

Developments in, and improvements to SSR, have been substantially supported by the 'boffins' of Malvern, and have foundations in the early WW2 work there.

Rebecca and Eureka

This system was developed by TRE at Malvern and tested at Defford.

It was a short-range radar navigation system used for accurately dropping airborne forces and their supplies.

It had two parts, the 'Rebecca' airborne transponder/receiver, and the 'Eureka' ground–based transponder. 'Rebecca' calculated the time it took for 'Eureka' to return its signal, giving the range and, via a directional aerial, the relative location.

Production began in 1943 and it was first used to drop supplies to resistance fighters in occupied Europe.

The name 'Rebecca' was an amalgamation of, 'recognition of beacons' and 'Eureka' the Greek for, 'I've found it'.

The road to Defford airfield is still called Rebecca Road.

BABS

The 'Beam Approach Beacon System', (BABS), was developed alongside Rebecca to allow instrument approaches to be flown at an airfield.

The ground beacons used for initial trials at Defford were based on IFF sets. This system later enabled the world's first automated-landing at Defford described in the previous chapter.

The 'Radar War'

TRE was also at the centre of a 'ghostly' war, fought amongst the airwaves, a war of jamming and detecting.

The 'tit for tat' measures and countermeasures drove innovation at a ferocious pace because lives depended upon keeping one step ahead of the enemy.

Below are just some of the many inventions produced by TRE.

A bomber crew needed to know if enemy radar was scanning for it so that evasive action or other countermeasures could be taken. By its nature, ground radar produces a very large signal; therefore British planes were equipped with a small receiver, called 'Boozer', which lit a warning-light in the cockpit if it detected a radar signal.

Whilst this wasn't totally effective in large bombing raids, when every enemy ground-radar would be turned on, it proved very useful in smaller missions that flew deeper into Germany.

It could also pick up German night fighter radar transmissions.

* * *

Once the enemy radar was detected, there were options developed to confuse it. 'Moonshine' consisted of a receiver fitted in a fighter plane that re-transmitted the original enemy signal after delaying and distorting it to produce a much larger return, making a single bomber appear to be many.

It was very effective when first used, with the Luftwaffe expending time and fuel hunting 'ghost' bombers, but the German operators learnt how to spot the false planes.

This caused 'Moonshine' to be shelved for a period but it was brought back into action prior to D-Day to produce false ship signals.

'Moonshine' sets were fitted into a number of small launches, possibly at Tewkesbury boat yards, and subsequently 'produced' a fake invasion fleet in the English Channel, right where the Germans were expecting it – one of several successful tricks played to make the Germans move their forces away from Normandy.

* * *

H2S was used in a countermeasure to Nazi night-fighter attacks on British bombers.

By the spring of 1943, bomber losses were mounting and it was apparent that the Germans had found a way to direct their single-seat night-fighters into the bomber formations using radar.

The obvious defence against this would be a way of warning bombers of the approach of a night-fighter.

The first attempt at producing such a device was known as 'Monica', which produced a cone of radar coverage from, and behind, the tail of the bomber. An approaching fighter caused 'pips' on the bomber's communication system.

However, this had some serious deficiencies. It could only detect aircraft within the rear cone of transmission and could not indicate height, speed or position of the approaching aircraft.

The close formation of bombers also caused false 'pips' that occurred so often that aircrew often turned 'Monica' off.

Bomber losses continued to mount; numbering five hundred and eighty-four in the first four months of 1943, with lighter nights approaching that would assist the Germans in spotting targets. An investigation showed that the prevalent approach of fighters was from underneath in order to silhouette the bombers against the night sky.

One evening in mid-April 1943, during a walk on the Malvern Hills, the problem was mentioned to Lovell who had been unaware up to that point.

Lovell suddenly thought of using H2S, but with a modification to remove the 'blank' area of the display. A prototype indicator was built at Malvern, tested at Defford and almost immediately detected an approaching fighter.

One of the new indicators was then fitted in a Halifax whilst a Mosquito simulated dummy attacks.

The fighter produced a radar echo giving its range and bearing accurately. By the beginning of July the new indicator was in production. It was christened *'Fishpond'*.

Once fitted, the device saved many lives by alerting bombers of approaching enemy night-fighters. It was also discovered that the Germans had succeeded in producing a device called *'Flensburg'* which detected *'Monica'* transmissions but not *'Fishpond'*. Therefore *'Monica'* was hurriedly removed from bombers and *'Fishpond'* installed.

* * *

Fig 55
Fishpond indicator Type 182a on Lancaster

'Window' was born of the realization that strips of metal, or wire, cut to exactly half of the wavelength used by a ground radar, caused a distortion on the receiving scanner proportionate to a square sheet of metal with each side equal to the strip length.

When discharged from a plane the strips gave a false reading on enemy ground radar screens, such that two or three bundles produced a false echo equivalent to a four-engined bomber.

As we have seen, British Scientific Intelligence had expended considerable efforts to learn the nature of German Ground (*'Freya'* and *'Wurzburg'*) radar systems and knew the wavelength they used, predominantly 50cm.

Most effective were strips of black paper backed with aluminium foil, cut to 27cm x 2cm and packed into bundles weighing one pound. These lightweight strips of 'chaff' fluttered slowly to the ground, causing maximum interference.

'Window' was so effective in trials that it was initially banned from use! This was for two reasons, in case the Germans learnt of it and used it to launch another Blitz, and because proponents of radar were worried that it could undermine the case for further radar development.

It was subsequently discovered that the Germans had actually made the same discovery and banned it for the same reason!

In a bizarre standoff, for over a year the curious situation arose where both sides knew how to use chaff to jam the other side's radar but had refrained from doing for fear of their opponent replying in kind.

'Window' was finally ratified for use by Churchill in June 1943, for deployment from July, the state of the war then being that further large-scale bombing raids by the Luftwaffe were unlikely, whereas the British concentration bombing campaign was in full-swing but suffering a significant bomber attrition rate.

'Window' was initially employed in the firebombing of Hamburg.

Twenty-four bombers were equipped with the strip bundles and led the main group, discharging the packages at a rate of one a minute through the flare chute, timed by a stopwatch. This created a 'smokescreen' for the following main bomber force.

The result was spectacular, with radar-guided searchlights and anti-aircraft guns firing randomly and the German night fighters failing to find the main bomber force.

As a result bomber losses were cut by around half from the norm. Bomber crews, desperate for anything that helped protect them, quickly adapted special discharge chutes for the strips.

'Window' became known as 'chaff' because that was the nickname used by the Americans. Their system was slightly different because it used a device that gave the strips an electrostatic charge as they were expelled. The charged strips repelled each other, ensuring that they did not stick together.

'Window' was later used in a D-Day diversionary tactic.

A 'phantom' invasion fleet, heading for Boulogne, was created by aircraft heading towards the French coast, dropping the metal strips whilst performing a series of circular turns.

The signals thus created were detected and enemy action was directed towards it and away from the Normandy beaches.

'Chaff' is still used to confuse radar guided missiles and was deployed by British Naval vessels in the Falklands War.

Most modern military aircraft and warships have chaff-dispensing systems.

Glyn Warren recounts an incident involving 'Window' trials at Defford in his book 'Endless Skies'.

It was decided to trial firing 'Window' out of an aircraft door in the hope of confusing approaching enemy night fighters.

The aluminium foil strips were placed in an extra-long 'Very Pistol' cartridge and fired out of the open door of a Lincoln.

The following aircraft watching the trial reported a very long silence thereafter, then a report of, 'returning to base'.

It transpired that no one had thought about the air pressure suction with the Lincoln door open, and the pressure had sucked all the foil strips into the aircraft creating a vortex, covering all the occupants with tin foil and obliterating the instruments.

* * *

'Mandrel' was a jamming device used against German 'Freya' Ground Radar. It was carried in a percentage of a bomber force and when in close enough formation, the signal would combine to screen the whole force.

It produced 'white noise' and was constantly modified to match the varying frequencies used by the Germans to try and counter it.

It was used throughout the war with great success.

* * *

It was necessary to assess the effect of countermeasures such as jamming on German Radar, and this was the primary role of another Worcestershire location, Guarlford Listening Post, just outside Great Malvern.

The location was probably chosen because it had the best radio reception in the area.

It was a secret site, surrounded by a high wire fence with armed guards, and was self-sufficient, having its own water supply and septic tank.

The facility was run by the RAF and was linked into the Radio Counter Measures Group at TRE Malvern. It consisted of a brick-built building which is still just about standing, containing a variety of receivers, and four large latticework radio masts.

The post listened into German radar station wireless telegraphy communications that used simple, easily broken, coding.

One of the greatest successes of the listening post was to identify that a significant Nazi radar unit had moved to Peenemunde from the French Coast, and the subsequent investigation revealed the importance of the V2 rocket testing site, which was later bombed.

The 'Dinner Wagon'

TRE received a very special request, codenamed *'Dinner Wagon'*, in August 1944.

It specified that a glider be equipped with both radar and communication equipment to enable it to be landed as part of an assault and operate in three capacities, as an Early Warning Station, Night Interception Station and Fighter Direction Station.

A Horsa glider was chosen and fitted with two radars, one British, one American, together with facilities for both VHF and UHF communications, Identification Friend or Foe, radar displays, telephone facilities and a power generator.

The project was undertaken at RAF Defford using two RAF aircrew and ten radar mechanics, and was given top-priority, access to RAF Maintenance Units and the Defford workshop resources.

It was completed by 11 November 1944 and the glider was then towed by a Stirling bomber to RAF Wethersfield in Essex.

Upon arrival it was made operational within an hour by TRE staff who had travelled on the Stirling, and was being demonstrated later that evening.

Due to the advanced state of the war, *'Dinner Wagon'* was not used greatly in World War Two, but the concept of air transported ground radars formed part of future military thinking.

* * *

Another use of an H2S unit modified for the purpose at Malvern and operationally flown from Defford, occurred in the run-up to D-Day.

The success of the invasion depended on the Germans believing that the main attack would come across the Straits of Dover.

A number of 'deceptions' were used to achieve this, but just one unjammed German Radar unit on the Normandy coast could have blown apart the whole strategy.

Ten days before D-Day, an intelligence report arrived on a Thursday evening, suggesting that just such a German radar unit was in operation.

TRE Malvern built a detector for the enemy radar the following day, and by Saturday it was installed and tested in a Halifax with a further test-flight taking place on the Sunday.

The following Monday night, an operational flight of the Halifax from Defford flew up the English Channel scanning the French coast and confirmed there was no such radar unit in operation.

This was probably a record for an operational requirement to be translated into an operational use, and a very rare operational sortie from Defford.

* * *

TRE also engaged with the Army prior to D-Day in the field of detecting tank movements by radar.

A scientific breakthrough at the Air Defence Research and Development Establishment (ADRDE), at Pale Manor, demonstrated an ability to detect moving vehicles.

The mode of detection was coupled with a H2S unit in a trailer and towed to Jubilee Drive, Malvern, where it was pointed down at the nearby railway tracks. It detected the trains.

The following day the trailer was hauled up the Malvern Hills near to the Worcester Beacon. A convoy of vehicles was driven in and out of Malvern at a point where the modified H2S had an uninterrupted view and it clearly detected the convoy.

The unit was then fitted to a Defford Halifax, but it required an extremely accurate navigator to get decent results and was shelved.

After D-Day, the stalling of the Allied advance, and the fear of Rommel and his tanks reinforcing the western front, reignited the need.

This time TRE tried a K Band H2S with a six-foot scanner and demonstrated 'staggering' results at low altitudes, between 1,000 and 2,000 feet.

On 10 January 1945 in a demonstration, the unit accurately detected the movements of groups of tanks, although acceptance was delayed by six weeks, as the observers believed that a covering of snow had been the cause of the good result.

Once the snow melted a similar result was obtained, and fitting to Mosquitos commenced, but the war in Europe ended with only three operational uses successfully conducted.

The Americans and Malvern

The Tizard Mission resulted in the Americans setting up a 'radiation laboratory' at MIT (Massachusetts Institute of Technology) – one of the world's most prestigious universities.

They sent Liaison Officers to the UK – not in uniform due to their country's non-combatant status.

After the Pearl Harbour attack, and America's entry into the war, a Radiation Laboratory outstation was set up at Malvern, with TRE clearing some huts in the grounds of the Boy's College.

The new unit was called, 'The British Branch of the Radiation Laboratory', (BBRL).

As the BBRL did not deal with electronic countermeasures, and this was a significant part of RRE work, a further unit was set up, linked to the Radio Laboratory at Harvard which was the American establishment involved in this work in the USA.

They were housed in huts at Malvern near to the TRE Countermeasures Group. This unit was called 'The American-British Laboratory of Division 15', (ABL). Division 15 was part of the US National Defense Research Committee.

These units worked together with TRE on a number of projects.

One was the development of a very powerful ground radar, the *'Microwave Early Warning Radar'*, (MEW), using American equipment.

The MEW was used in defending against the Nazi 'flying bombs' and after the war, at Heathrow Airport in civil aviation.

Swords into Ploughshares – TRE Post-War

A number of versions of H2S were declared obsolete at the end of the war, although six continued in trials at Defford or in use by, for instance, the Army.

The main line of progress was that of H2S Mk IX/IXA for V-bombers. The first engineered sets of H2S Mk IXA for V-bombers were flight-tested from Defford in the summer of 1951 in Hastings or Ashton aircraft as the V-bombers were not yet available.

In 1956, this version of H2S entered service in the Vickers Valiant, followed by the Avro Vulcan and the Handley Page Victor.

It had the name 'NBC', (Navigation and Bombing Computer) and was a composition of H2S and a computer system.

The 3cm H2S Mk IXA remained with the V-bombers until they were retired from service a quarter of a century later.

In 1956, Valiant V-bombers used H2S Mk IXA in a pre-emptive strike against the Egyptian Air Force at Cairo Airport.

On 1 May 1982, a Vulcan used this system in the Falklands War in a pre-dawn attack on Port Stanley, dropping 21, 1000lb bombs on the airport. This was the last operational use of a system descended directly from that born and tested at Malvern and Defford forty years earlier.

The modern-day AWACS, (Airborne Warning and Control System) system also began at Malvern and Defford.

This was in the form of a Hamilcar glider fitted with two engines which had a very large radar in an enormous radome especially built at Malvern.

This was the first form of AWACS for long-range detection of aircraft, especially at high altitudes that granted greater detection distances. It was very difficult to fly, and getting engines fitted into a glider meant the controls were split between the front and rear cockpits. Thus it required two pilots, one at the front, the other at the rear, with half the controls each, linked by an intercom that luckily didn't fail!

* * *

Once the war was over, Malvern Boy's College returned to its original function, so TRE had to leave.

The decision was made for Malvern town to remain as its home and TRE occupied a wartime naval training building in St Andrews Road, Malvern, called 'HMS Duke'.

The Boy's College commenced its return to normality in 1946, although some parts remained requisitioned until the 1950s.

The abrupt end to the Japanese war also terminated a number of TRE projects developed for use in the Far East.

Suddenly, many staff were no longer required, and 'de-mobbing' began.

E.H. Putley in his book, *'Science Comes to Malvern'*, recalled,

> 'Some wanted to return to their pre-war jobs. Others to return to college to complete their education. A lot were transferred to atomic energy at Harwell while others were made redundant......1946 seemed to consist of nothing but farewell parties.'

A.P. Rowe, the famous wartime director of TRE, emigrated to Australia for health reasons and later became Vice-Chancellor of Adelaide University, before returning to live out his days at Malvern, and becoming a part-time teacher at Malvern College where a laboratory was named after him.

He was briefly succeeded by his Deputy, Dr. W. Lewis, who initiated a two-part post-war electronics research programme, that set the direction for TRE thereafter.

One part featured radar, in the guise of advanced weapon systems such as missile guidance and reconnaissance using both optical and infrared methods.

A new Physics Department progressed the other prong of research into the Electromagnetic Spectrum, from visible to infrared, meteorology, early electronic computers and as described elsewhere in this book, the brand new science of Radio Astronomy.

A number of modern-day essentials had their roots at sleepy Malvern.

These include the radar weather maps beloved by television weather reporters, Police Speed Cameras, Thermal Imaging and Passive Infra-Red, (PIR), Lighting Units.

A major legacy is the use of wartime radar developments in civil aviation, including aircraft identification stemming from 'Identification Friend or Foe', Air Traffic Control instruments and *'Automatic Pilot'* and landing systems.

Many of these inventions were tested at Defford, and later, Pershore airfields.

The Air Defence Research and Development Establishment, (ADRDE), worked after the war on nuclear accelerators, the linear accelerator, and were also responsible for building a *'Synchroton'* atom-smashing machine at Malvern in the 1980s.

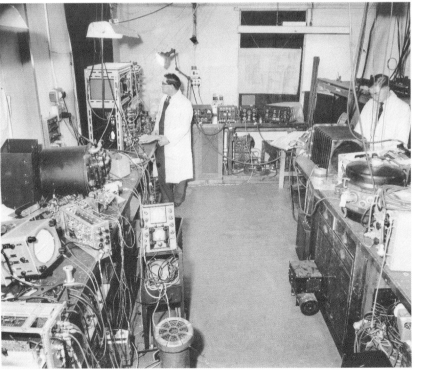

Fig 56 Visit of Queen Elizabeth 24/4/57

Fig 57 Laboratories Malvern 1960

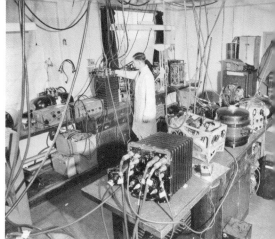

Fig 58 and Fig 59
Laboratories Malvern 1960

Fig 60
Laboratories Malvern 1960

Fig 61 *Design Floor Malvern 1960*

In 1953, TRE was amalgamated with the Radar Research and Development Establishment, (RRDE), and became the Radar Research Establishment, (RRE).

In 1957, a young Queen Elizabeth visited, and granted a royal charter upon the establishment, which became the Royal Radar Establishment.

The photographs opposite, taken in 1960, evoke the scientific atmosphere and are probably every layperson's idea of what a research laboratory should look like!

Some personal memories of Malvern and TRE

Simon Young is now working in a police staff role at Defford, and has always been particularly interested in the history of the airfield because of the links his father and mother had to TRE.

He recalls his father,

'My father's name was David John Young. He was actually known by everyone as John and was born on the 29 January 1927 in the High Wycombe area.

During World War Two, as a sixteen-year old teenager, he moved to the Malvern area, on his own, and joined the Ministry of Defence, (MOD), around about 1942-43. Initially he was just doing low-level scientific research but he was an exceptionally bright and educated man and even studied for degrees in later life. Because he was in the MOD he was not required to sign up for the services but I believe that he was in the Home Guard at Malvern where he lived in an apartment in the town above some shops in a place called Warwick House.

My father was always very secretive about his work but I believe that he was involved with something to do with the creation of infrared markers which enabled planes to land in the dark during the war.

There were a number of MOD sites in the area, with the biggest one being what was called the 'South Site' in Malvern.

My father got married in 1950, at the age of twenty-three years, to my mother Sheila who was just twenty at the time. In the 1950s and 60s he worked at Defford, and Pershore, and

eventually established himself as a scientist in a senior position. Post-war he worked mainly on radar and infrared projects.

Some of the work was really ground breaking stuff, for instance one of the original silicon chips was developed at Malvern, as well as microchip technology. I remember my father once had a prototype of an LED, (Light Emitting Display), watch which was in kit-form and was later developed by the Sinclair Company.

He also travelled abroad a lot in the 1960s and visited places like Aden and Cyprus working on scientific projects to support the military.

Fig 62 David and
Sheila Young

Fig 63 David Young
during testing flight

Fig 64 David Young
(centre) with
colleagues and
Handley Page
Hastings WD482,
RRE Pershore

In 1970, he took me to RAF Bedford and showed me the inside of a DC10 aircraft kitted out like a laboratory, full of electronic equipment.

He finally retired in 1987 whilst working for DERA at the Malvern site.

My father passed away on the 4 January 2005.'

Fig 65 Douglas Dakota DC3 believed at Pershore

Fig 66 Group photo at Pershore with Handley Page Hastings – David Young in centre with white shirt

* * *

David Young's wife, Sheila, was born in Coventry and, after a spell living in Birmingham, she moved to Malvern in 1936. She recalls,

'I first met John (David), my husband, in 1947. I was on a day-trip to the seaside at Weston and he was on my coach. He was flirting with me a bit which I wasn't used to!

I was just seventeen years old at the time and he was about twenty, and he later asked me to go and see a film with him. We also went dancing at the Winter Gardens where Joe Loss used to play – John was however an awful dancer!

When we first met, John was already working in the TRE at Malvern as some sort of laboratory assistant. He was taking examinations all the time, including eventually obtaining a BSc Degree, and in time became a highly qualified scientist.

We got married at Christ Church in Malvern on the 24 September 1949.

Later on he went to work at Defford but because he had signed the Official Secrets Act he never talked about his work, other than that he was involved in the development of radar. I knew that his work was experimental but no more. He loved his work and was very committed. There was no such thing as overtime and John used to do a lot of night flying but he would just get up and go to work as normal next day. Sometimes I could see him getting frustrated but he had a job to do and got on with it.

I once went to a formal mess evening for staff at Defford. Some people were in uniform and John was there as a guest – I seem to recall that they had some very nice raffle prizes!

After finishing at Defford he moved to Bedford before retiring. During this period he visited RAF bases all over the world and went to such places as Aden, Singapore and Gibraltar.

We had two sons, Simon and Tim, who both became police officers.'

Sheila was awarded an MBE in 2000 and has played a significant role in local politics, as did John in later life.

* * *

Colin Bryan further recalls,

'My brother-in-law's father, Norman Harris, deceased, worked for the Royal Radar Establishment at the South Site at Malvern.

He had a long employment with them having started when they were based at the beginning of the war on the south coast. He was moved to Malvern when the Government thought it was too risky leaving them so close to the coast. They ended up living in one of the many 'prefabs' they hurriedly built in Malvern to house all the 'boffins' that descended on the town.

What work he was involved in will probably never be known but he was a very skilled engineer and draughtsman. I do know he had something to do with the design of the central array of the large radio telescopes sited at RAF Defford when they were upgraded in the 80s.

I can recall that I applied for an engineering apprenticeship at TRE/RRE when I left school aged sixteen years, and had to attend for an examination day at the 'North Site.'

The engineering section was very impressive. It was incredibly well laid-out with all the engineering tools, lathes, milling machines and workbenches. It was spotlessly clean and tidy as I remember. I didn't get the job however and went on to get an apprenticeship at a Worcester Company.'

* * *

Philip Read recalls,

'After RAF Pershore closed in 1977 I transferred to Malvern Royal Radar Establishment as a "heavy fitter" travelling around to different sites and helping scientists fit equipment onto the top of aerials. They were usually extremely high up and cold and windy at the top. Normally you were lifted part way up on a truck, following which you would climb up a ladder on the outside. At the top you pushed a hatch open with your head to reach the section where the equipment was installed. The first time I went up I froze, I was that scared, and don't know how I got back down again. As time went on however I conquered my fears and routinely ran up the inside of the structures to get to the top.

At one stage I was obliged to transfer to Malvern North Site to work again as a mechanic in the 'MTRI' section but after eighteen months I managed to move to a vacancy in the "Vacuum Section" at Malvern.

Some of the equipment being used by scientists could be up to three-quarters of a million pounds in value and it was essential for them to conduct their experiments in a totally dust-free and sterile environment, which is where we came in. We had to be meticulous in our work and sometimes used things like helium to find leaks that might introduce foreign substances into a test environment. It was actually a really interesting job and I thoroughly enjoyed the work.

Eventually the establishment I was working in was taken over and privatised by QinetiQ but I carried on working there until retiring at the age of seventy-two years.'

* * *

Chris Pell recalls,

'I left University radio astronomy research in 1974 to attempt to discover what the "real" working world outside of University was like. My first job after University was with the Plessey Company, majoring on radar. I was fortunate to have an excellent first job in industry and a great boss, (as an aside, he had been a WW2 Mustang pilot and drove his clapped out Triumph Spitfire, with NO seatbelts, as if it was a Mustang fighter), who introduced me to many aspects of technology and defence, including RRE/RSRE.

My work with Plessey focused mainly on IFF, SSR and novel applications of the technologies. This allowed me to begin working with some of the 'boffins of Malvern', and was a great experience for a young applied scientist. So much so, that I was offered a permanent position as a government scientist at RSRE, Malvern in late 1978, causing me to "jump ship" and join the Scientific Civil Service.

I arrived at Malvern on an extremely cold and snowy Sunday evening, 2 January 1979, if my memory serves correctly. My young wife and very young son were not able to join me as I took up temporary residence in the Apprentice's Hostel at the old County Hotel in Great Malvern.

Suffice to say that this was most certainly not a 5 star hotel, but was steeped in history and, most probably, some of the longer-term residents had been there since WW2. After about four months I was able to buy a house and we became a family unit once more.

Working as a young scientist at RSRE, initially at the level of a Senior Scientific Officer, was an immense privilege and tremendously professionally rewarding. In many ways it was not unlike being at University with enormous freedoms as to what you did, but with a substantial research budget – it almost seemed too good to be true, and you actually received a salary for having technological excitement! But, of course, there was the serious side of delivering novel ideas and solutions to improve the performance of the sensors for the defence of the UK, and also providing technical support to advanced sensor procurement programmes – remember that at the time the Cold War was still real and there was much UK and NATO investment in ground-based and airborne sensors, particularly radar.

At the time of my arriving at RSRE, many of the wartime scientists had left the Establishment on retirement; although several remained and were due to retire in the near future. Malvern clearly had its characters, all of whom were extremely intelligent and capable scientists, and many had world-leading reputations in their respective fields. Innovation and a strong commitment to your scientific work seemed quite natural.

It is very tempting to write a lengthy account of the "mad scientists", but this would take a complete book on its own. Suffice to say, for example, that there were: Geoff who started his career at Malvern as an apprentice but became a brilliant self-trained mathematician who also excelled in bell-ringing and was an expert in operating a 1930's telephone switch board; Nigel who could, and indeed did, solve anyone's problems with high power radar transmitters: "Pussy" who answered the phone "Mieow" and wore a cat's tail at work; Phil who was ahead of anyone in the earlier days of digital data transmission ... and so on.

Don't forget that the ubiquitous LCD, (Liquid Crystal Display), displays of today all owe their origin to the Malvern Physics Department scientists. Non-conformity frequently just seemed to breed brilliance.

I was lucky enough to have some seven years at RSRE Malvern and these were probably the most intellectually rewarding years of my career, and also a very happy time for a young family in Malvern. Though, it was at times tough on one's family, since work at the Establishment was a continuum and frequently intruded into all seven days of the week. However, times were changing and non-technological innovations such as focused research, a customer-supplier relationship and budgetary pressures and full economic costing/control all began to affect us.

I left Malvern in 1985, at a time when many others were also deciding that it was time to move on – it was changing quite dramatically, but I will not enter into the debate here as to whether this assisted technological innovation or not. After a very brief spell back in industry, I continued in Government

Fig 67 *Chris Pell in Harrier 2*

scientific service for another 20 years, having positions at the Royal Aerospace Establishment, Farnborough, in the "Centre" of government in Whitehall, in Washington DC and again in Whitehall as the chief scientist of the Royal Air Force.

I was fortunate to have a stimulating, at times exciting and a largely rewarding career, and for much of this I must thank RSRE Malvern.

Very fond and truly special memories.'

Fig 68 Chris Pell in Harrier 2

* * *

The concentration of so many brilliant scientists at Malvern during the war and thereafter, demonstrably evolved into a high-powered creative group that truly embraced the 'holistic' principle, that the whole is greater than the sum of its parts.

Those who worked there recall a happy place, despite great adversity and pressure, a place of innovation, groundbreaking inventions and a scientific focus and intensity that belied its location in a sleepy town in the shadows of Elgar's Malvern Hills.

Chapter Three

Pershore Airfield – 'From Moth to Vulcan'

IN JUNE 1934, Pershore Airfield was established when former Flight Officer R.J. Bunning bought Tilesford House, an Elizabethan farmhouse, and the surrounding farmland.

The site is situated seven miles from Worcester, and five miles from Evesham, with the Bredon Hills in close proximity to the south.

In addition to his RAF experience, Bunning had previously also been the Chief Instructor at the *'Northants Aero Club'*, the *'Norfolk and Norwich Aero Club'* and the *'Cardiff Flying Club'*.

He formed *'Worcestershire Flying School'*, entitling the aerodrome he created as *'Lilesford Aerodrome'*, although it came to be known simply as *'Pershore'*.

The flying school offered courses, using Cirrus II Moth planes flying from the grass field, from beginner pilot courses, to that of obtaining an instructor's certificate, and pupils could be accommodated in the farmhouse.

The subscription rate was £1 per annum and the rates for dual instruction, for example, were forty shillings an hour.

At the outbreak of World War Two in September 1939, the Air Ministry realised that they would need to expand their airfield programme and explored potential sites in Worcestershire. Although in normal circumstances it was too far away from the coast for planes to operate in a front-line capacity, the County was an ideal location in which to train pilots and aircrew.

* * *

In 1939, the airfield at Pershore was requisitioned and construction of what became RAF Pershore began in earnest in 1940, using labour drawn from the firm Wimpey & Co.

Three runways forming an 'A' pattern were constructed; runway one of 2,000 yards, (1,829 metres), bisected by Long Lane, runway two of 1,510 yards, (1,381 metres) and runway three of 1,405 yards, (1,285 metres) in length.

Four T2 Hangers and one J-type hanger, along with a Control Tower, which was also known as a Watch Office, were added, as well as four hexagonal brick and concrete pillboxes around the perimeter. These particular constructions housed light machine-guns which were designed to protect the base from attack from land.

One of these pillboxes was sited to cover the main approach to the base along Throckmorton Road.

All of the living quarters and training accommodation were based within RAF Pershore itself, with the exception of the WAAF quarters, which were in Pinvin, about a mile from the airfield.

WAAF Josette Demy née Bens, described some of the challenges she faced in Glyn Warren's book 'The Endless Sky – Pershore and Defford'. She completed her training at Innsworth Lane, Gloucester and was then posted to Pershore.

On arriving at the railway station, on her first day, she walked two miles in the rain to arrive at the camp and was struck by the fact that there were no houses, and that they were in the middle of a field with only a few Nissen huts.

Josette was put in a new hut, with four other girls, and they had to cross the camp through muddy ground to get to it. It consisted of a corrugated iron roof with a concrete floor.

Washing facilities were about half a mile away and early each day they had to get across the field to wash.

After breakfast, their uniforms were inspected by the Duty Officer, and then they were marched off to the RAF camp to carry out their duties in what was a twenty minute trek uphill.

There is evidence that the construction work attracted the attention of Germany's Luftwaffe and in 1945 a high-flying reconnaissance photograph taken from a Junkers aircraft, of the construction site, was found in a disused printing works, close to the Bergen-Belsen Concentration Camp in northern Germany, by a Mr. Marshall. It had apparently been taken in 1940.

The area around the site at Pershore was actually bombed by the Luftwaffe on several occasions.

On the 11 September 1940, and 12 October 1940, high explosive and incendiary bombs were dropped near the airfield, and one unexploded bomb had to be dealt with.

On the 22 November 1940, one hundred and fifty incendiary bombs were dropped, some of which landed just a quarter of a mile away from the site.

On completion of construction, the Officers' Mess and living quarters were sited on the northwest side of the airfield, together with a Sergeants' Mess and Quarters, and the Airmen's Quarters.

There were Flight Officers and Crew-Rooms, Rest Rooms, an Armoury, Parachute Stores, a Gas Clothing Store, and Motor Transport Sheds. To the south of the airfield was a Bomb Store.

* * *

On the 6 February 1941, an advanced party from the RAF arrived at Pershore, followed on the 24 February 1941 by Squadron Leader R.A. Williams, Senior Admin Officer, who took command of the station.

From February 1941 until 1944, RAF Pershore was home to No. 23 Operational Training Unit (OTU) for Bomber Command crews, many of them Canadian, flying Vickers Wellington bombers.

Even before the first aircraft arrived, the Luftwaffe attacked the airfield on the 16 March 1941, causing some damage but no injuries.

On the 9 April the first Wellingtons arrived at Pershore.

The Wellingtons were known as the 'Wimpy', the nickname being taken from the friend of the cartoon character 'Popeye the Sailor'. They were produced in greater numbers than any other bomber and were known as the last of the 'cloth' bombers. It was not unknown for Wellingtons to return to RAF Pershore with bits of fabric hanging from the frame of the plane after coming under attack.

Ron Makinson was a Sergeant Airframe Fitter, and in Glynn Warren's book recalled one German attack.

The first four Wellingtons had arrived on the 9 April and as the perimeter track was still not complete the planes were marshalled on each side of one leg of a runway, not in use, and the petrol bowsers were also placed in this area.

It was there that a lone German plane dropped an, 'HE' bomb, the shrapnel from which hit the two petrol bowsers.

In May 1941 the airfield at Defford was taken over as a training satellite for Pershore.

* * *

In keeping with other training units, No. 23 OTU took part in several leaflet-dropping operations, which were known as *'Nickels'*, over occupied-France, along with raids over Germany, including those at Essen, Bremen, and Dusseldorf.

Coupled with operational losses, and a high accident rate at RAF Pershore, the large Canadian War Graves section in Pershore Cemetery pays testament to the sacrifice and bravery of those who lost their lives.

One of those first accidents occurred on 27 June 1941 when a Wellington crashed on the verge of the great North Road, three miles north of Bawtry.

The port engine failed one hour into a flight but after the pilot managed to get the plane onto the ground, the tail gunner Sergeant Kellough was trapped as a fire broke out. He later died of his injuries in hospital.

During World War Two, a total of 55,573 men died in Bomber Command which is more than all those who serve in the whole of the RAF today.

* * *

Sergeant Ron Makinson described another more humorous story when, during a particularly cold spell, some personnel needed more than a little coaxing from a warm hut, in the middle of which was a large round stove.

A Flight Sergeant kept sending a runner to get them out but to no avail and the report came back that the door was 'jammed' and they couldn't get out.

The standoff was resolved when one of the Sergeants took the smoke charge out of a Very Light, went up on the roof and dropped it down the chimney, before putting a brick on top.

In less than thirty seconds the door flew open, complete with the frame, as the people inside launched themselves at it in an effort to escape the fumes.

In thick smoke, some even came out through the windows!

Finally he went on to describe an accident that occurred on the 20 October 1941, when aircraft began to return to the base.

One of them, fully bombed-up, blew a tyre on landing, and as the undercarriage collapsed, it belly-flopped and caught fire.

All the crew got out and ran as fast as they could to get away from the fire and then the bombs started to go off due to the heat.

Large pieces of the aircraft were sent flying through the air with the force of the blast, some of which came down onto the hanger roofs, which, due to being steel, added to the cacophony.

* * *

On the 18 May 1942, the Defford OTU satellite was, as we have seen, taken over by the Ministry of Aircraft Production and some of the Pershore staff were posted elsewhere, leaving them with the capacity to run only three training flights from the station.

In the same month RAF Pershore participated in what became known as the '1,000 Bomber raid on Cologne', when Air Marshall Sir Arthur Harris assembled every bomber he could muster from frontline RAF units, reserves and operational training units.

In all 1,047 aircraft formed part of the operation of which nearly two thirds were Wellingtons.

RAF Pershore contributed some thirty aircraft, and had the added challenge of being one hour's flying time away from even reaching the English coast.

The first day of the operation took place on the 27 May 1942, and was judged to be a major success. Forty-one RAF planes were lost in all. One of those planes was a Wellington N 2857 'F' which took off from Pershore with a Canadian and Australian aircrew.

They were shot down by German fighter planes over the Dutch coast and there were no survivors. Sergeant W.R.C. Johnson, the Canadian pilot, and his crew of four, lost their lives on their very first operational flight.

All of the other planes returned safely to RAF Pershore, although the tyre of one burst on landing.

A second similar large-scale raid took place on the 1st/2nd June 1942, and this time the target was Essen.

Thirty-three aircraft on Pershore's strength took part, of which eighteen flew from RAF Pershore itself.

Despite adverse weather conditions, and the effects of German air and ground defences, the raid was judged to be satisfactory.

On this occasion two Wellington bombers from Pershore failed to return, and their crews were lost. The first was believed lost over the sea, and the second was shot down over Holland.

The third, *'1,000 Bomber raid'*, took place on the 25 June 1942, and the target was Bremen.

Seventeen Wellingtons from Pershore were involved in the operation, of which eight were made up entirely of pupil crews, four were instructor crews, and the remainder mixed.

They all took off from RAF Pershore and experienced extremely difficult flying conditions. Twelve of the planes reached and bombed the target area, despite these difficulties, as well as technical problems with some of the aircraft.

On this occasion two aircraft failed to return with the loss of both crews, one over the sea, and the second once again shot down over Holland.

Flight Sergeant W.R. Hughes, who was later awarded the DFC, recalled some of his memories of that operation, and life at Pershore, in Glyn Warren's book.

In his logbook he recorded taking off from Pershore at 2240hrs, in operations against the enemy, as part of the *'1,000 Bomber raid'*.

At one point his plane was intercepted by a Heinkel HE 111, which they shook off by using evasive action, without damage to their aircraft, and they carried on to drop bombs on the prescribed target. The total duration of flight was 7 hours 15 minutes and they arrived back at Pershore at 0544hrs.

Hughes had arrived at Pershore in April 1942 as a screened Flight Sergeant Air Gunner having previously flown in Blenheim night-fighters during the Battle of Britain, then Wellingtons in 149 Squadron, followed by a tour with 70 Squadron in the Middle East.

He also recalled how the posting to Pershore as an instructor changed his life. On one flight from the airfield he nearly took the chimney pots off his future wife's home in Pinvin!

* * *

As the pace of the war continued, RAF Pershore continued to play a full role in the war effort as sadly accidents continued to occur leading to loss of life. These included a couple where, by some quirk of fate, dinghy's carried inside the plane in the event of a crash over sea, inflated and damaged the planes structure.

On the 31 July 1942, seven Wellington bombers based at Pershore took part in a raid on Dusseldorf, with a mixture of experienced and trainee aircrews.

The attack was successful but on this occasion one plane failed to make it back home, although fortunately the crew of experienced instructors all managed to bale out of the aircraft successfully. They were taken as Prisoners of War.

This pattern of operations and loss of life continued, whilst back home daily life also went on in a very ordered manner.

Defence of the airfield was a critical element of that work and in addition to a well-trained defence force, all sorts of tactics were applied to confuse enemy bombers.

One of the deployments was to man 'dummy flare paths' in the fields using what was described as a 'goose-necked' flare with paraffin. The irony of the fact that the men manning these sites were trying to encourage the Germans to bomb them instead of the actual airfield was not lost on them!

On the 16 November 1942, Pershore took over the satellite airfield at Stratford, following which 23 OTU again rose to a full establishment. This was maintained until January 1944 when it reduced to three-quarter strength to allow major works to take place at Pershore.

At the end of January 1943 approximately seventy-five members of the RAF Regiment participated in an exercise with the local Home Guard. They moved out of RAF Pershore in the morning and succeeded in 'capturing and destroying' Pershore Railway Station and the Atlas Works which had been held by the local 'Dad's Army'.

On the 29 May 1943, yet another tragedy unfolded as a Wellington bomber, participating in a 'Wings for Victory' fly-past over Pershore Town, shed a wing and struck a house, and the 'Brandy Cask Hotel', in the town, before coming to rest.

Five people on board lost their lives.

The plane was on the strength of Pershore, but had flown out of Stratford on that date. The fire-tender racing from Pershore to get to the scene of the crash took a bend too fast and overturned, injuring the crew.

On the 2 August 1943, Wellington BK 504, whilst engaged in landings and circuits, crashed near Pershore Town, having approached the runway too high. Despite efforts to retain control of the aircraft after it overshot, it crashed and caught fire on impact, with the loss of the crew. On board at the time was a sixteen-year old ATC Cadet, Raymond Carter of 1046 Squadron, ATC Wolverhampton. He is believed to be the youngest member of aircrew to be killed in Worcestershire during World War Two.

Not all of the casualties at Pershore came about as a result of flying, and on the 17 December 1943, the Duty Marshall Officer walked into the revolving propeller on the starboard engine of a Wellington. He died of his injuries the following day.

On the 15 March 1944, No. 23 OTU disbanded and was absorbed into No. 22 OTU at Wellesbourne, Mountford, who also took over the satellite field at Stratford.

RAF Pershore was transferred to the control of Ferry Command.

* * *

Between March 1944 and 1948, No. 1 Ferry Unit operated from the airfield and their role was to transport various aircraft from factory to front-line operational units overseas.

Because it was a support function the aircrew got less recognition than their operational colleagues, but they were extremely busy and in May alone they delivered one hundred and thirty-eight aircraft on routes overseas.

* * *

On Friday 12 October 1946 the wife of Flight Lieutenant Jess Ernest Crosse received a formal invitation from the Officer Commanding and Officers of RAF Pershore to attend a dance. The dress code was 'evening dress' with the event due to start at 9pm.

Her invitation card is held within the Archive Section of the RAF museum in Hendon.

147

* * *

In 1947, the UK was subjected to very severe winter conditions and Pershore was one of the few stations not to close down. The water tower froze up and burst whilst, due to a lack of coal, only one cookhouse was operational. The Sergeants' Mess kept warm by burning a tree purchased from a local farmer.

No. 1 Ferry Unit left Pershore for Manston on the 17 May 1948.

* * *

On 15 January 1952, No. 10 Advanced Flying Training School formed at Pershore, and remained until 1954, training pilots and aircrew in Airspeed Oxfords.

On 14 April 1954, the unit disbanded and the airfield was given to the Ministry of Supply. For the next three years the facilities at Pershore were enhanced, including the creation of a design office, laboratories and workshops, whilst the main runway was extended to 7,500 feet.

The extension of the runways, to cater for jet planes, met with some opposition from local farmers who wanted to preserve farmland.

Despite the protests, runway 04/22 was extended on the southern end from its wartime length of 2,000 yards to 2,450 yards.

* * *

The Radar Research Flying Unit (RRFU), used the base from early April 1957 until 1976, as various types of aircraft, including Hastings and Canberras were moved from Defford.

In September 1957, the Royal Radar Establishment (RRE) moved its staff from Defford to Pershore, where the facilities were better, and the runway could accept aircraft that Defford was unable to accept due to runway size.

On the 9 December 1957, Canberra WK 129 took off from Pershore to participate in radar trials off the North Wales coast.

The plane flew into bad weather, with snow and rain falling, and eventually radio contact was lost.

Following a search by other aircraft, and mountain rescue teams, the plane was found to have crashed fifty feet below the

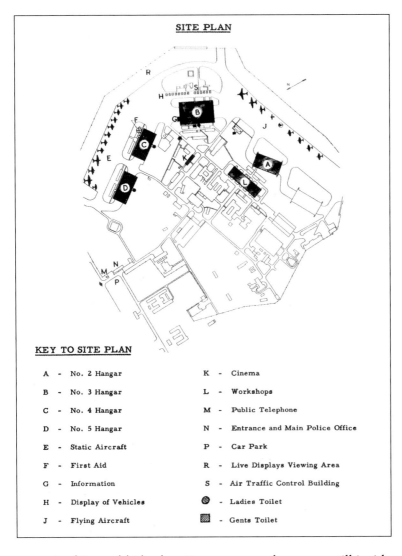

SITE PLAN

KEY TO SITE PLAN

A	-	No. 2 Hangar	K	-	Cinema
B	-	No. 3 Hangar	L	-	Workshops
C	-	No. 4 Hangar	M	-	Public Telephone
D	-	No. 5 Hangar	N	-	Entrance and Main Police Office
E	-	Static Aircraft	P	-	Car Park
F	-	First Aid	R	-	Live Displays Viewing Area
G	-	Information	S	-	Air Traffic Control Building
H	-	Display of Vehicles		-	Ladies Toilet
J	-	Flying Aircraft		-	Gents Toilet

Fig 69 RRE Pershore Plan

summit of Carnedd Llewlyn. Two crew members were still inside the wreckage both of whom were dead.

* * *

Paul Dallimore has further recollections of his father Thomas James Dallimore,

> 'In 1957 everyone was transferred to RAF Pershore and my father carried on doing the same job. He serviced lots of different aircraft.

From what he used to tell me he was the only aircraft electrician at Pershore who was cleared to fly in the jets. I know that he went up in the Canberras. He had to have a medical every year, and also do some training at Boscombe Down where he was immersed in a tank of water and they had to get into a dingy.

He had his own flight kit which he used to bring home the day before a flight. Being an eight year old I used to try it on, including wearing the helmet and face mask. My dad thought it was funny one day to put his thumb on the end of the air tube. He nearly suffocated me and needless to say I didn't see the funny side of it – in fact for years I had a phobia about face masks.

We were still living in the same place and my early memories were of going to the kids' Christmas party at RAF Pershore in one of the hangers. I was about five years old. We went there in a military green Leyland bus. There were lots of kids there from the Air Ministry families.

Then when I was about ten years old I recall watching aircraft flying in and out all day. My father used to work late for night flying and used to come home at silly times. Sometimes there were flights to RAF Lossiemouth in Scotland and we had kippers that were brought back. They used to carry them in the bomb bays which they had to open afterwards to take the smell away. He was made an honorary member of the Transport Command Squadron and wore a badge with this on.

I remember the Vulcans coming in to land, as Pershore was a dispersal airfield, and they would also practice "Quick Response Alerts". They had separate accommodation for the aircrews and even though our house was four or five miles away it used to shake when they came into land.

In those days I thought nothing of getting on a bike with my friends and going to the perimeter fence at RAF Pershore, armed with a couple of jam sandwiches. We would hang around on the road barrier and watch Jet Provosts doing 'circuit and bumps' coming in to land, touching down, and taking off again.

We couldn't get onto the site because they were very strict, except for 'family days' when we would visit. One of my friends, Steve Hall, was the son of an MOD Police Sergeant, who was often on the front-gate. On one of the visits my dad took me around and sat me in a Canberra.

When I was a bit older in about 1970 I used to go to Defford. You could still get onto one of the runways. I learnt to drive there but you had to watch out for the odd pheasant or the nuns from Croome who were an absolute menace in a car!

During this period some of the Pershore aircraft, aircrew and ground crews were sent on detachments and my father went to Laarbrook in Germany and even Libya before relations with Gaddafi went sour.

I believe that he also met one of the Concorde pilots, as it was a diversionary airfield for testing purposes.

I also seem to recall that one of the Hastings that flew from there was flying up and down the North Sea throwing things out of one of the doors. I think it was something to do with global warming research but my dad wouldn't say anymore. He was always very secretive about what he was doing and quite strong-minded.

When RAF Pershore closed around 1976/1977 my father transferred to Malvern, albeit he was then seconded to work at Defford working on the 'Golf Balls' for a while.

He worked his career out inside, wiring stuff up for The Royal Signals Regiment, which he wouldn't talk about.

He finally retired in 1988 and passed away in 2003.'

Here are more of Tom's photographs during his time at Pershore.

Fig 70 *On detachment at Pershore with Gloster Meteor. Tom seated 1st on right*

Fig 71 *At Pershore*

Fig 72 *Royal Flight at Pershore. RAF Flight personnel with Pershore ground crew in their "whites". Aircraft is DeHavilland Heron*

Fig 73 *Her Royal Highness Queen Elizabeth the Queen Mother at Pershore*

Fig 74
Christmas Party, Pershore, year unknown

Fig 75 Pershore October 1974. Aircraft appears to be a Vickers Varsity with an additional "equipment pod" fitted

Fig 76 Servicing a Canberra engine

Fig 77 Meteor NF12. WD790 with non-standard thimble nosecone, now at North East Air Museum

Fig 78 Recovering a Sea King after a forced landing

Fig 79 "A"
Flight Pershore
in front of what
appears to be a
long nosed
Canberra

Fig 80 Champers
at the end of a
successful trial.
With Gloster
Meteor

Fig 81 With
English Electric
Canberra WH660

* * *

Eric Robinson was a Squadron Commander at RAF Pershore from 1958 to 1961 and during this period flew a variety of aircraft on research and development for the experimental establishment at Malvern. He commented online about a BBC programme in 2014 that,

> 'Pershore was a very happy and friendly station. We lived in wooden huts as married quarters for a time before moving out to rented homes in the town itself.'

* * *

In an article in the 'Air-Scene UK' magazine in 2006 Mick Freer commented,

> 'My love affair with the English Electric Canberra dates back to the days when I was still at school – I would sit watching Canberras in the circuit at the nearby Royal Radar Establishment (RRE) Pershore in Worcestershire.
> During the summer holidays, I would cycle to the airfield, prop my bicycle against the Ministry of Defence security post and sit and watch the flying. The Police were very tolerant of me and left me alone, provided I didn't take photographs.'

* * *

In 1961, the base made local headlines when the Ministry of Aviation won the right to remove the spire from St. Edburga's Church at Abberton, which they claimed was a danger to planes flying into Pershore.

The spire was demolished and kept inside RAF Pershore for some years, with the intention that it would be re-erected at some stage, but after Pershore closed it was found to be structurally impossible to replace.

* * *

In the 1960s, there was anything up to forty aircraft and five hundred personnel working at Pershore, their job included aircraft servicing, and the building of bulky equipment such as scanners. By the time it closed, over five hundred aircraft, covering seventy different types, had been processed through the workshops there.

Personnel were involved in the installation, and testing, of a range of electronic equipment, including airborne interception and maritime radars, navigation and bombing systems and guided weapons sensors. Also developed were reconnaissance systems such as synthetic aperture radar and infrared line scan.

On Saturday 18 May 1963, the *'Royal Radar Establishment – Aircraft Department Pershore'*, held an *'Open Day'* at Pershore and a *'Note on Pershore Air Station'* in a hand-out described its work,

> 'The Ministry of Aviation air station at Pershore houses the Aircraft Department of the Royal Radar Establishment. The function of this department is to fit experimental equipment to aircraft, carry out test and development flight trials and to service that section of the M.O.A. Air Fleet allotted to the establishment. The department is organized into three divisions – engineering, experimental and flying – with administrative support, and is staffed in the main by Ministry employees of various grades. The aircrew effort required is provided by the Royal Air Force, and in addition certain firms under contract to the Ministry maintain a resident technical and experimental flying staff.' *(Malvern Museum)*.

❊ ❊ ❊

It should be remembered that some fifty people were killed whilst engaged in radar trials in aircraft operating from Defford and Pershore.

Bill Sleigh was formally a Chief Engineer at Pershore, having previously been the deputy to Mr. D.K. Henderson, a man who was regarded by many as being a far-sighted engineer.

Bill subsequently donated a Roll of Honour listing all those who gave their lives flying with the TFU, and its successor the Radar Research Flying Unit, to the National Trust.

In 1988 William H Sleigh produced a comprehensive two hundred page report entitled *'Aircraft for Airborne Radar Development'* which provided a historical and detailed insight of the first involvement of aircraft in 1936 through to Defford, during and after the war years, and the future development of Defford.

His report also dealt with aircraft types, as well as engineering aspects, which was his specialism. A copy of this report is held in the Archives Section of the RAF Museum in Hendon.

* * *

Retired police officer Colin Bryan recalls,

> 'Being a Malvern lad I took an interest in all things RAF being an Air Cadet in the "187 City Of Worcester Squadron" and ended up as an Adult Warrant Officer after going through all the cadet ranks.
>
> I had many a flight from RRE Pershore in my cadet years. We used to hitch-hike from Worcester and present ourselves at the Police Gate at Pershore and then get signed in to the RAF Crew Room where, if we were lucky, the 'boffins' gave permission for us to join them, and the RAF crew, on their test-flights in either a Vickers Viscount or a Handley Page Hastings.
>
> Both aircraft were kitted out inside with Dexion shelving where all their electronic wizardry was mounted. We took the spare seats at the back, for take-off, but once airborne spent most of the time on the flight deck standing between the pilot and co-pilot. Flying in the Hastings required the issue of a parachute harness and a chest-pack parachute.
>
> I never knew what the kit was that they were testing and dare not ask questions about any of it.
>
> Besides the big stuff the RAF also flew a fleet of Canberra bombers from Pershore which were also used for radar research trials, but they wouldn't let us go in those.
>
> If there was no flying we used to go to the control tower and spend the day there, watching all of the visiting aircraft coming in for touch-and-go landings.
>
> The majority of these were either Jet Provosts or Folland Gnats from RAF Little Rissington.
>
> If you were lucky you might get a Phantom or Buccaneer make an appearance.

I also remember a Fleet Air Arm Gannet being there for test flights with new radar kit on it.

I also saw a Nimrod which was probably there for testing the 'Airborne Early Warning' kit they were developing. That came to nothing when the powers that be finally bought Boeings with the circular radar disc mounted on top of it to become the RAF's AWACS platform.

I still have my old ATC logbook for some dates for flying from RRE Pershore between 1967 and 1971. Co-incidentally my first-ever flight was in the Viscount 661 from Pershore, and I was bitten even more by the flying bug after that.

My logbook shows 31.10.67 Viscount 661, 1.11.67 Viscount 661, 4.1.68 Hastings 482, 9.4.69 Hastings WD 499, and 3.9.71 Viscount 661.'

Fig 82 Vickers Viscount XT661

Fig 83 Colin Bryan 187 Squadron RAF Aberporth 1973 with Bloodhound missile

* * *

Philip Read recalls memories of RAF Pershore,

'In 1967 Tony Benn was the Government Minister in charge of the Ministry of Technology which was part of the civil service.

I got a job in October 1967 as a mechanic in the Motor Transport Repair and Inspection Section at RAF Pershore. There was about seven of us in the section and the man in charge was always referred to formally, and with due respect. We repaired Fire Engines, "Queen Mary's", which were artic-like wagons that carried wings, tractors, towing tugs, cars, and runway sweepers – the runways had to be swept every day.

Fig 84 *Defford & Pershore RRE MT Drivers Xmas Party*

RAF Pershore was very secure with a perimeter fence all the way around it and Ministry of Defence Police controlling the entrance and exit gates, where we had to show our passes. That said, RAF Pershore actually had a road running through it, which was closed off every time planes landed or took off.

I had an interest in planes and was fascinated to see all the different types visiting the base, many of which are now consigned to history.

On another occasion I saw a Lightning come in and the pilot put a show on by literally climbing vertically before landing and casually getting out of the cockpit with a briefcase in his hand.

Fig 85 Vulcan in flight

Fig 86 Vulcan nosecone containing H2S radar

Bird-strikes were sometimes an issue and on one occasion I saw a Harrier coming over Bredon Hill and saw a puff of smoke. These planes only have one engine and it had suffered a bird-strike. The pilot managed to glide it in to RAF Pershore.

On yet another occasion a Gnat Trainer was hit with such force that a bird finished up going through metal and into the cockpit. Fortunately the pilot was able to land although it is fair to say that crashes did sometimes occur, but mainly in the Welsh hills.

RAF Pershore was also used for the Queen's Flight to land as well as being a standby airport for the Concorde flight trials if it ever experienced any difficulties.

Viscounts and Canberras also did a lot of experimental flying from Pershore for radar development as well as Photo Reconnaissance planes.

All in all it was a very busy place with lots of uniformed RAF personnel about as well as scientists in plain clothes.

There was a practice that when the RAF flew back from Scotland they used to bring fish back with them, and when they went to Cyprus it was oranges.

The base itself was like a factory – there was a blacksmith, welders, aircraft fitters – there was even a plastics shop which made the nose-cones for Nimrod aircraft.

In 1973 I was part of a large group photograph in front of a Nimrod wearing my fashionable flared jeans befitting of that time period.

I finished at RAF Pershore in 1977 when it closed down as an operational base, following a defence review.

The last plane to fly out of RAF Pershore was a Buccaneer aircraft.'

* * *

Canberra WT333 served with the RRE at Pershore between 1969 and 1977 and was one of a large contingent based there. They were considered to be the most suitable aircraft for radar research, as work could be carried out on the front fuselage without affecting its operational capacity.

One of the base's final roles was to act as a dispersal airfield for Vulcan Bombers, should NATO go onto a high alert.

Throughout the 1960s when the UK had its own airborne nuclear deterrent, Pershore was one of many dispersal airfields used by the 'V Force'. The aircraft used to arrive, usually three at a time, and sit in readiness on a dispersal pan at the eastern end of the runway. The planes would sometimes sit for days and then suddenly scramble and take off in a stream. Separate accommodation was built for these aircrews in the southwest corner of the airfield and they were totally independent to the RRE.

* * *

Pershore had its own Ministry of Defence Police Force detachment as well as a Fire Brigade which was highly equipped and were on stand-by at all times when flying was being conducted.

After flying ceased at Pershore the Fire Brigade was approached to see if they wanted to take on the role of providing airfield security – and they then took on a dual role.

Whilst the Fire Brigade was fortunate over the years not to have been involved in major incidents leading to loss of life, they were involved in two significant incidents.

In the first a Valiant WP 200 overshot the runway in April 1961 and ended up with the perimeter fence wrapped around its nose-section. The rescue operation to extricate the crew took hours to carry out.

The second incident occurred on 7 June 1976 when Buccaneer XN 975 had engine problems on approach and hit an old aerial mast. One of the Fire Brigade, an ex-member of the RAF Fire Service, actually detected a problem in the engine tone of the aircraft as it approached.

* * *

By 1972, the use of Pershore was declining and the RRE was transferred to the Royal Aircraft Establishment at Bedford.

The closure of Pershore was announced as early as 1972 for run-down into final closure in 1976.

In 1976, the RRE became part of the Royal Signals and Radar Establishment (RSRE) and the rest of the aircraft at Pershore, nineteen planes in all, moved to Bedford.

The airfield actually officially closed in December 1977, and the last aircraft to leave RRE Pershore on the 9 December 1977 was Buccaneer XX 897.

The responsibility for closure fell to Mr. D.H Moseley the last Works Manager.

The perimeter fence was then moved, cutting off the ends of runways one and two. Vulcan bombers no longer shook the town's crockery.

Fig 87 The total workforce of Pershore in front of a Nimrod prior to closure of RSRE Pershore

Chapter Four

'A Window
on the Heavens'

THE DEFINING feature of Defford that remains today is the single radio telescope on its rails, a lonely silhouette on the edge of the airfield.

Closer inspection of the sign adorning the fence surrounding the telescope reveals the following,

> 'This installation is part of MERLIN – A National Facility for Radio Astronomy operated by the University of Manchester for the Particle Physics and Astronomy Research Council.'

This sign represents the culmination of a journey that began before World War Two, and grew directly out of the developments in radar and associated technology at Malvern.

This book has no pretensions to be a scientific treatise or manual, therefore the science of radio astronomy is described at a somewhat superficial level, but in order to understand the continuing presence and importance of the Defford telescope, it is necessary to lightly step through the history and nature of radio astronomy and the MERLIN project.

There are many textbooks available to describe all aspects of radio astronomy, both at a summary lay-reader level, and also in great scientific, technological and mathematical detail. However, it is worth mentioning just one book, which was written by Dr. R. C.

Jennison, later to become Professor, entitled simply *'Introduction to Radio Astronomy'*.

Radio Astronomy is a branch of astronomy that uses radio frequencies to study objects in outer space. It had no name until 1959 when the International Telecommunications Union gave it official recognition as Radio Astronomy.

Radio frequencies (RF), similar to light, occupy a particular part of the extensive *'electromagnetic spectrum'*, (EM) but are generally characterized by having a somewhat lower frequency, or longer wavelength, than the light of the visible spectrum as seen by the human eye.

The EM spectrum actually extends from the very lowest frequencies of the Extremely Low Frequency (ELF) at around 3Hz, up to the ionizing radiation of the very highest frequencies in the Gamma Ray spectrum. Out of interest, the radio frequency (RF) part of the EM spectrum is frequently considered to extend from around 3 kHz (known as Very Low Frequency) to about 300 GHz (known as Extremely High Frequency), that is from 3000 Hz (or cycles per second as it would have been referred to originally) to some 300,000,000,000 Hz!

The key issue is that any radio communication, radar or radio astronomy device, employing a receiver, must have a response 'tuned' electronically to the selected part of the RF spectrum of interest.

Perhaps at this point a 'health warning' should be given! The reader might already have noticed references to both *frequencies* and *wavelengths*. To the practitioner, be it a scientist, an engineer or a technician, there is a natural and almost automatic interchangeability between *frequency* and *wavelength* and, in general, there is no confusion or ambiguity. However, to the casual reader this can be most confusing! Suffice to say that one is, essentially, the reciprocal of the other, with a relationship related to the velocity of light. Quite simply, the higher the frequency, then the shorter the wavelength and, conversely, the lower the frequency then the longer the wavelength.

Radio Astronomy began with an accidental observation of a natural phenomenon, but the main foundations stemmed from the by-products of radar research during World War Two.

Initially, radio astronomy observations, either accidental or deliberate, would have been confined to lower radio frequencies, but have subsequently been extended and developed to encompass microwave, through millimetre wavelengths to even higher frequencies. In fact, almost the entire EM spectrum is now of interest to astronomers, even Gamma Ray, the very highest frequencies.

Radio waves from an astronomical object, the Milky Way, were first detected in 1932 by Karl Jansky at Bell Telephone Laboratories. This discovery was an unforeseen outcome of his investigation of static that interfered with short-wave transatlantic voice transmissions.

Jansky was using a large aerial that to the lay person resembles a giant coat-hanger many feet across, mounted upon the wheels of a Model T Ford to allow easy rotation. He was using this contraption to scan the heavens for crackling noises from thunderstorms. However, when Jansky listened to the receiver output on an ordinary loudspeaker there was a steady hissing sound that did not decrease below a certain level but varied during the day.

By revolving the aerial he discovered that the greatest sound or signal came from a certain fixed location relative to the stars, not the earth or sun. This location was the centre of our galaxy, which has the greatest concentration of stars. Jansky concluded that without doubt, he was listening to the sound broadcast by the Milky Way.

Radio Astronomy is conducted by the use of large radio antennas otherwise known as radio telescopes. They can operate as a single unit or can be linked in order to employ two scientific techniques known as 'interferometry' and 'aperture synthesis'. The advantage of linking telescopes is that a much higher angular resolution power can be achieved regardless of individual unit size, by varying the distance between linked units.

Jansky did not progress his discovery of radio emissions from the Milky Way because Bell Telephones assigned him to another project. However, he inspired a number of other scientists to begin researching radio wave emanations from celestial bodies and for his original observations he is frequently credited with being the *father of radio astronomy*.

Two of the most important scientists inspired by Karl Jansky were Sir Bernard Lovell and James Stanley Hey, a British Army research officer who made the first detection of radio waves emitted by the sun on 27 February 1942. Hey is a particularly important figure in the history of the Defford telescopes.

The next major development in the new science of radio astronomy was the creation of a radio-physics group at Cambridge University comprising J.A. Ratcliffe and some members of the Telecommunications Research Establishment from Malvern who had worked on radar during World War Two. However, it should be noted that, at around this time, the new and exciting science of radar astronomy began to inspire many wartime scientists and engineers and various embryonic research groups formed across the world.

A number of advances followed, including the pioneering of interferometry and, subsequently, aperture synthesis techniques and the harnessing of the power of early computers during the late 1960s and early 1970s to enable greatly superior radio astronomical techniques and resulting observations, including the creation of larger effective apertures.

By way of example, the *First Cambridge Catalogue of Radio Sources'*, produced by Martin Ryle, ex TRE Malvern and later to become Sir Martin Ryle and the Astronomer Royal, in August 1950 recorded some fifty radio sources in the Northern Sky at a wavelength of 3.7m using a long baseline interferometer. Perhaps to indicate just how challenging the technological task was at that time, subsequently, most of the sources were deemed to be the result of 'confusion' – a salutary reminder of the inherent dangers in the potential ambiguities present in a simple interferometer.

Two famous, important and comprehensive surveys of radio sources – the '2C and 3C' surveys produced maps of the radio sky.

'2C' – The Second Cambridge Catalogue of Radio Sources', was completed in 1955, comprising a list of 1,936 sources between certain declinations. It too did, however, contain some anomalies and was superseded by *'3C' – The Third Cambridge Catalogue of Radio Sources'* in 1959. There were two later revisions, *'3CR'* in 1962 and *'3CRR'* in 1983.

Radio Astronomers employ many different techniques and methods to observe objects in the radio spectrum. The simple technique is to point an antenna at a radio source to analyze its emission. However, in order to 'image' a region of the sky in more detail, multiple overlapping scans can be pieced together in a computer-processed mosaic. The kind of observation instrument required varies significantly according to the type of information sought on the source, the signal-strength and the level of detail sought.

Many modern radio observatories inhabit remote, elevated, arid – and sometimes quite exotic – places such as Arecibo in Puerto Rico, the extinct volcano of Haleakala, on the Hawaiian island of Maui, and the Roque de los Muchachos Observatory in La Palma in the Canary Islands. This is because there are various natural phenomena that can interfere with the signals. The Earth's ionosphere, a region of earth's upper atmosphere from around 60km to 1000km altitude, can inhibit low frequency or long wave transmission. Water vapour interferes with higher frequencies, and of course other earth-based transmitting devices may cause interference.

The science of radio astronomy has led to a major increase in knowledge, and has revealed the existence of new objects including:

- Pulsars, a highly magnetised rotating neutron (collapsed core) star or white dwarf (star core remnant) that emits a beam of electromagnetic radiation)
- Quasars, (basically a supermassive black hole found in the centre of most galaxies)
- Radio Galaxies, (a compact region at the centre of a galaxy that emits very high level of radio emissions)

These discoveries have been possible because radio astronomy allows the detection of phenomena not visible in optical astronomy. These objects contain many of the most extreme and energetic physical processes in the universe.

Radio astronomy has also been used to detect and observe cosmic microwave background radiation, the Sun and solar activity, radar mapping of the planets, observations of Sagittarius A – the galactic centre of the Milky Way, and of merging galaxy clusters. It has also allowed the detection of many molecules existing in inter-stellar space, including water vapour.

This book explains how the 'sleepy backwater' of Defford is still linked directly to the sound of the universe!

The Story of James Stanley Hey

Dr Hey is closely connected to Malvern, (TRE) and (RRE), as well as to Defford, and the two radio telescopes originally sited at the airfield.

Hey was born in 1909 in Lancashire, third son of a cotton manufacturer. He studied physics at Manchester University, eventually obtaining a master's degree in X-Ray crystallography. He was a physics teacher before World War Two.

In 1942 Hey was trained at the Army Radio School and joined the Army Operational Research Group, working in the field of radar anti-jamming methods. This was a priority because German jamming of Allied Radar during the previous year had become a serious problem, highlighted by the success of Nazi jamming from locations on the French coast in assisting the escape of the German warships 'Scharnhorst' and 'Gneisenau' through the English Channel.

In February 1942, Hey made the discovery that the maximum jamming interference seemed to correspond with the sun and, having checked with the Royal Observatory, realized that a very active sunspot was travelling across the sun at such times. He concluded that sunspots could emit metre-wave radiation, a finding corroborated in the USA the same year.

In 1945 Hey was engaged in the tracking of V2 rockets approaching London. He found an apparent anomaly – transient radar echoes that continued after the V2 rocket attacks ceased. He concluded that the readings were generated by ionized meteor trails, which radar could track day and night. Hey demonstrated that every meteor leaves a trail in the upper atmosphere, which reflects radio waves as effectively as a metal wire. Hey's third discovery came from an experiment where he decided to map cosmic radio waves, resulting in the creation of a map of the Northern Sky with the Milky Way as the most prominent feature. However he discovered a fluctuating signal in one section of the sky that he deduced correctly to be a radio signal from a single source. It was later found that the fluctuations were caused by the Earth's ionosphere whilst the actual signal was coming from a steady and powerful source subsequently identified as Cygnus A, now recognized as one of the most powerful radio galaxies.

In 1949, Hey became Head of the AORG, and in 1952 he returned to the Royal Radar Establishment at Malvern where he continued his radio astronomical work. His work there concerned obtaining the positional accuracy of astronomical objects via radio methods and determining various performance limitations caused by radio interference, radio reflections from the upper atmosphere and the factors affecting radio propagation.

Hey was Head of the Research Department from 1966 until 1969 when he retired.

The first radio telescope built by Hey was at Malvern, a parabolic reflector fifteen metres in diameter, mounted on a German 'Giant Wurzburg' mount, probably moved to England after the end of the war.

This radio telescope accurately observed the movements of the first Russian Sputnik satellite in 1957. Chris Pell, a radar scientist who has made a number of contributions to this book, recollects that he was actually in Malvern at this time, with his parents, and was taken to the radio telescope at 'North Site' on the Sunday morning and heard the Sputnik sounds.

Hey subsequently made accurate radar observations of the Moon. The method employed was to use a high power transmitter at Malvern to bounce pulses off the Moon which were received by the University of Texas in order to provide lunar surface information.

The Defford Radio Telescopes

By the late 1950s, radio astronomy techniques had found a military application in the tracking of Soviet ballistic missiles. The RRE allocated funding for Hey's team to design and build two radio telescope dishes to be mounted on redundant railway lines laid on the disused main, and east-west runways at Defford airfield.

In an article in the 'New Scientist' magazine on 4 January 1962, Dr Hey reported as follows,

> 'A radio telescope interferometer, comprising two mobile and steerable radio telescopes with 25 metre (82 feet) dish reflectors, has recently been installed by the Royal Radar Establishment on the site of a former airfield at Defford, near Malvern. The equipment is to be used for research into the phenomena of our space environment observable by radio and radar methods... Research of this nature **is vital for any future applications, military or civil, involving missiles or vehicles in the Earth's upper atmosphere or space.** Within a Government establishment such research can be appropriately directed.'

Defford was still a *'Top Secret'* establishment protected by the Official Secrets Act and the above statement, in bold type, requires little imagination to understand why. This was the *'Cold War'* era, and the potential for tracking Soviet Intercontinental Ballistic Missiles and other similar weaponry is clear.

An interferometer is the name given to a family of techniques in which, usually electromagnetic, waves are superimposed causing interference in order to extract information.

Interferometry is used in many scientific fields but for the purposes of this book its use in radio astronomy is the key purpose. For example, Interferometers are used across many scientific and industrial applications for the measurement of small displacements, refractive index changes and surface irregularities.

An Astronomical Interferometer consists of two or more separate telescopes that combine their signals, offering an angular resolution equivalent to that of a telescope of diameter equal to the largest separation between its individual elements.

The interferometric process was, and is, a highly attractive technique, although it must be remembered that it is not completely equivalent to having a continuous and fully-filled antenna aperture of the spacing distance of the interferometer elements. Modern Radio Interferometers consist of radio telescopes separated by large distances but connected by various methods.

Improvements in the stability of radio telescope receivers and reliable communications in the 1970s allowed worldwide and even earth orbit telescopes to be connected to conduct *'Very-Long-Baseline Interferometry'* (VLBI).

The use of modern synchronisation methods allows remote radio telescopes to be combined to synthesise a single antenna that is in effect the size of the earth.

This is all a very long way from J.S. Hey's two motorised telescopes on parallel tracks, but still employs the same basic principles.

The two main VLBI systems in operation today are the 'Very Long Baseline Array' in North America, and the 'European VLBI Network', which has telescopes in Europe, China, South Africa and Puerto Rico.

Others exist in Australia and New Zealand – the 'Long Baseline Array', and the 'East-Asian VLBI Network' (EAVN), in Japan, China and South Korea.

The detailed science of interferometers is beyond the scope of this book but Dr. R. C. Jennison's book provides an excellent summary of their principles of operation.

* * *

The 1960s installation of the two radio telescopes at Defford was originally designed to complement those at Jodrell Bank and Cambridge with the aim of delivering versatility and accuracy.

The Defford telescopes had parabolic reflectors enabling ease of change of wavelength by changing the critical element (feed) at the focus of the large parabolic dish, and the ability to operate at wavelengths as short as 10cm, due to their good surface accuracy. The fact that they were linked and mobile on their tracks made them a 'variable spacing interferometer' that could change the angular resolution in any direction required.

Dr Hey stated that the Defford telescopes would be used for several types of research, including the investigation of radio transmissions from 'radio stars', the Sun, Moon and planets. The upper atmosphere of the earth would also be examined by scrutinizing its effect upon radio waves and obtaining reflections from 'free electrons' contained within meteor trails, various regions of the ionosphere, and aurorae.

The famous Birmingham Company of 'F.H. Lloyd' was responsible for providing major elements of the telescopes. In an article on the company contained on 'History website.co.uk', Birmingham Community Historian, Dr. Carl Chinn recounts,

'In the 1960s Mech(anical) & Elec(trical) (Department) was involved in the electrical power wiring for two radio telescopes on a disused airfield at Defford near Malvern. The steelwork was supplied and erected by Carter Horsley of Tipton; the main contractor was Werkspoor of Holland. The client was the high security radar research establishment at Malvern. We were told that these telescopes, known as Interferometers, were for studying the Milky Way. However, we suspected their true purpose was of a more military nature.'

The Defford telescopes were constructed of wire mesh and the contour of the dishes deviated by less than a quarter of an inch (6.35mm) from a true paraboloid curve. The reflectors were able to point in any direction with accuracy of over 3 minutes of arc. The structures each weighed 250 tons (approximately 226kg) and were 120 feet, (approximately 36.5 metres) in height. The dish aperture was 25 metres and operation was possible between wavelengths of several metres and 10cm.

The dishes were connected as an interferometer by cabling of high thermal insulation and stability housed in a concrete duct.

Movement was enabled via the railway tracks set 90 feet (approximately 27.4 metres) apart laid on the disused runway. Four 20 horsepower electric motors powered movement.

Running, braking, leveling and locking were controlled from one panel in a central laboratory. Celestial objects could be automatically tracked, and data was recorded digitally.

As the runways/tracks extended 750 metres from the intersection any relative position of the telescopes could be achieved, with a maximum spacing of between 700 and 1,200 metres.

* * *

In Volume 7 of 'Proceedings of Observatories', (Royal Astronomical Society – RAS), there is a resume of radio-astronomical research at the Royal Radar Establishment, Malvern between 1961, when the Defford interferometer was completed, and 1965. It describes some of the new system's capabilities.

'In addition to the research concerned with the reception of radio waves emitted by astronomical objects, the system is also equipped for radar astronomical investigations. The cabins mounted on the radio telescopes are large enough to accommodate two high power transmitters in addition to receiving and other equipment. The dual radio telescopes provide a very convenient system for radar astronomy not only because four transmitters can be installed, but also because one radio telescope can be used to transmit and the other to observe the radar echo.'

Fig 88
Commissioning of the Defford Interferometer 30.7.62, Dr Hey 1st left, Sir Martin Ryle, later Astronomer Royal, 2nd left, Sir Bernard Lovell 6th from right

The system was tested during the first part of 1961, and was ready later that year. Operations commenced with an investigative program in which the study of radio sources using the interferometer method was alternated at three-month intervals with radar-astronomical investigations including radar studies of upper atmosphere ionization.

Before the year end the new Defford system obtained never before seen radar echoes from meteor trains at the short wavelength of 23cm.

* * *

John Harris recalls his late father Norman Harris, and his involvement with the RRE at Malvern and Defford,

'When Dad was involved in design modification to the large dish he took a lot of black and white photos that were developed in their own laboratory on-site in Malvern. It must have been sometime between 1961 & 1963 as I remember going to visit the site with him, when I was on my school summer holidays, and being able to drive his car down the runway. I would then have to wait in the car while he checked the work progress – maybe it was all top-secret.

Some chap contacted Dad years later to ask about his memories of Defford as he was trying to compile its history. Dad explained that he still had a box of old photos showing the dishes mounted on rail tracks. The man called round to his house and took all the pictures.

When my wife Valerie worked at Morgan Motors she worked with another woman, June Smith. Her son worked in the control room at Defford and managed to arrange a guided-tour of the site, and we even climbed on to the big dish whilst it was moving. I can't remember who else was included on the tour but Dad came along with Val and me and reminisced about the work he was involved with.

He died on 3rd January 2010, just before my 60th birthday, aged eighty-nine years.'

* * *

During 1962 the Defford team concentrated on upper-atmosphere ionization by observing the *'incoherent scatter of radio waves by electrons'*, the only British research group to do so.

The team suffered a blow in November 1962 with the death of the team leader, Dr J.S. Greenhow, at the age of thirty-four years, a leading exponent of the study of the upper atmosphere by radar methods.

The upper atmosphere work continued in 1963 under Dr Colin Watkins who continued his scientific career at RRE/RSRE Malvern for many years, notably in the airborne radar area.

Chris Pell recalls him as, *'a highly respected, immensely proficient scientist with a most pleasant and agreeable disposition'*, and has very fond memories of working with him.

The Defford interferometer was also engaged in the study of radio sources with the manual analysis of results replaced with automatic digital recording and analysis via the RRE computer. This team was led by Hubert Gent and obtained measurements of very high accuracy, enabling the better identification of radio sources with optical objects and the identification of at least one error in a published optical position from conventional astronomy.

As an aside, Hubert Gent was a scientist of considerable repute, being the inventor of the *'Gent Lens'* – an electromagnetic wave lens for beam scanning. Again Chris Pell recalls him, *'distinguishing himself by being an avid snuff taker – a true gentleman, impeccably dressed'*!

A special study was also made of the radiation from Jupiter in order to determine radiation polarity, the emitting region shape, and the planet's magnetic axis inclination as against its rotational axis.

During 1965, the Defford telescope underwent alterations to enable new observations at the 10cm wavelength, with the aim of reducing the *'confusion level'*, enabling more accurate observation of sources.

It is apparent from the RAS report that even at this early stage the links between Defford and Jodrell Bank were being progressed, links that continue to the present day. There is mention of joint experiments and the setting up of a long-base interferometer with radio linking system between Jodrell Bank and Defford and the results thus obtained.

It is clear that the establishment of the two telescopes on their tracks at Defford was ground-breaking and began the long history that led to the MERLIN project, and the joint working with Jodrell Bank and Manchester University that underpins the purpose of the remaining telescope at Defford.

Jodrell Bank and Sir Bernard Lovell

The Jodrell Bank Centre for Astrophysics, of which the Observatory is part, is one of the largest astrophysics research facilities in the UK.

Originally called the Jodrell Bank Experimental Station, the Jodrell Bank Observatory was established by Sir Bernard Lovell.

Lovell went to the University of Manchester in 1945 in search of a site to study cosmic rays, an interest that stemmed from his radar work at Malvern during the war. A peaceful observation site was needed, and Jodrell Bank, twenty miles south of Manchester, was already owned by the university. It had been purchased in 1939 when the Department of Botany acquired three fields, and the site was extended in 1952 when a local farm was added, including the land where the Lovell telescope was later sited.

Jodrell Bank, a rise in the ground, was named after a local man, William Jauderell, an archer in the army of the Black Prince in the 14th Century whose descendants lived at a nearby mansion.

In 1945 Lovell was in Manchester attempting to use *'Gun Laying Radar'* from World War Two to investigate cosmic rays, but was prevented from doing so by electrical interference from the trams in nearby Oxford Road.

It was not just captured German equipment from World War Two, which contributed to the measurement and instrumentation in post war science, particularly, in the UK, the USA and Russia, but also the vast inventory of the UK's own war-surplus radars, radios and other electronic/electro-mechanical equipment which was a rich and valued source.

On 10 December 1945 Lovell moved the equipment to Jodrell Bank and used it to observe radio echoes from meteor trails.

Over the next few years, increasing amounts of ex-military radio equipment were taken to Jodrell Bank, including a portable cabin, known as a 'Park Royal', and a searchlight, upon the mount of which was mounted an array of antennas. This radio telescope was first used in October 1946, again for the observation of meteors.

In 1947 the 'Transit Telescope' was built at Jodrell Bank, at the time the largest radio telescope in the world. It was made of wire mesh suspended from a ring of scaffold poles that focused radio signals to a point 38 metres above the ground. This device was used to detect radio emissions from the Great Nebula in Andromeda, the first instance of an extragalactic radio source being identified.

In 1957, the 'Mark I' telescope, now known as the Lovell Telescope, was built. At the time it was the largest steerable dish radio telescope in the world. It used remnant gun turret parts from the battleships 'HMS Revenge' and 'HMS Royal Sovereign' in the motor system. This telescope was the only one in the world able to track Sputnik's booster rocket by radar, first locating it on 12 October 1957. The telescope subsequently tracked many space probes including, in 1960 the 'Pioneer 5' probe. It was used to transmit commands to the probe and also received data from it.

In February 1966 the Soviet Union requested that the telescope track the lunar lander, 'Luna 9', and recorded transmissions of photographs of the Moon's surface. Chris Pell recalls,

> 'This was quite a "steal" for Jodrell Bank since they published to the world the first lunar photographs before the Russians were able to do so!'

The majority of the telescope's time was however spent on scientific observations, including the use of radar to calculate the distance to the Moon and Venus, and the observations of pulsars and quasars.

The 'Mark I Lovell Telescope' has been upgraded many times and is still the third largest steerable telescope in the world, with capabilities far beyond those originally envisaged.

A further telescope, the 'Mark II', constructed in 1964, has operated as standalone, or as an interferometer with the Lovell Telescope, and is now used as part of MERLIN.

A 'Mark III' telescope at Wardle, near Nantwich, operated as part of MERLIN between 1966 and 1996 when it was decommissioned, whilst a further three telescopes were proposed but never constructed.

Jodrell Bank itself was placed on the UK Government's shortlist for World Heritage Site status and in 2012 the SKA, (Square Kilometre Array), Organisation moved its headquarters there.

Once completed, the SKA will be the world's largest telescope, combining thousands of dishes and other receivers spread across thousands of kilometres. It is also home to the MERLIN and now e-MERLIN projects.

Those interested in further exploring Jodrell Bank can visit the Jodrell Bank Discovery Centre which opened on Monday 11 April 2011.

MERLIN

The original MERLIN project has now become the e-MERLIN project. The acronym stands for the Multi-Element Radio-Linked Interferometer Network.

MERLIN is a linked array of six radio telescopes that when working together result in a very powerful telescope with an effective aperture of 217 kilometres. To put this in everyday terms, it could, upon inception, measure the diameter of a one-pound-coin from 100 kilometres away, and is an equal of the Hubble Space Telescope in capability.

The concept of MERLIN was born in 1973 when Henry Proctor Palmer suggested that the existing interferometer links at Jodrell Bank be extended. This was to overcome accuracy problems in identifying specific radio sources from outer space that were being experienced due to the limits of the baseline length of the interferometer. Palmer had been appointed Assistant Lecturer in Physics at Manchester University and spent twenty-seven years conducting research at Jodrell Bank.

The quest for increased resolution power led to collaboration between Palmer and the Radar Research Establishment at Malvern, resulting in the 82ft steerable telescope at Defford being radio-linked to the Lovell Telescope at Jodrell Bank.

In 1965 and 1966 this larger interferometer array led to the accurate identification of a number of hitherto unresolvable radio sources, but a number of quasars studied remained unresolved.

Subsequently the Mark I and Mark III, at Wardle, were linked and the plan was to increase the array at Jodrell Bank with further telescopes but these proposals failed to come to fruition due to financial constraints and political changes in government.

Thus Palmer suggested a number of smaller telescopes that could extend the North-South Jodrell-Defford baseline in an East-West direction. He named this concept the *four square interferometer* in his initial proposal. This idea evolved into the MERLIN system.

Construction began in 1975, and the array began operation in 1980/81, although Palmer left Jodrell Bank in 1979 and did not see his idea come to fruition. The system was originally called the MTRLI, (Multi-Telescope Radio Linked Interferometer), but was commonly referred to as MERLIN and the name stuck.

The base telescope for the original MERLIN system was one of two at Jodrell Bank, either the Lovell Telescope or the Mark II. The rest of the array comprised the existing Jodrell Bank Mark III based at Wardle near Nantwich in Cheshire, plus the Defford telescope, and a new telescope at Knockin, near Oswestry in Shropshire.

The construction of the new telescope at Knockin and the installation of microwave communication links and correlation equipment was Phase I of MERLIN, the funding for which was approved on 30 May 1975.

The Knockin installation was commenced on 9 July 1976 and completed on 8 October 1976, with the first remote control from Jodrell Bank taking place in January 1977. The microwave links were installed in May 1978 and the first observation using the system occurred in January and February 1980.

MERLIN Phase II added two further telescopes along with microwave links. These were sited at Darnhall and Pickmere, both in Cheshire.

Construction began on 9 April 1979 and completed by 31 October 1979. The two new telescopes were connected into the (MTRLI) MERLIN array on 20 July 1980, (Pickmere), and 16 December 1980, (Darnhall).

The Wardle telescope was dismantled in 1996.

In 1991 a purpose-built antenna at Cambridge was added, together with a number of improvements in the linking and correlation equipment. Subsequently the microwave links have been replaced by optical fibre links, increasing the sensitivity of the array thirty-fold.

The array is now known as 'e-MERLIN' and provides the UK contribution to the 'European Very Long Based Interferometer Network', which links telescopes across Europe and China.

The e-MERLIN project seeks to address:

'The history of star-formation and black hole growth as galaxies evolve

The physical processes which govern the formation of stars

The modes of activity in nearby galaxies

The energetic processes in relativistic outflows from jets generated by black holes and compact objects'

('e-MERLIN website e-merlin.ac.uk')

* * *

The importance of the remaining Defford radio telescope seems assured for the foreseeable future and it will continue to draw the eye of passers-by, as it has done for nearly sixty years.

It is a historical piece of immense scientific importance and heritage, still performing a vital function in astronomical research, and a tribute to the Malvern 'boffins' who conceived and built it all those years ago.

Chapter Five

'Endings'

Defford

The story of Defford did not stop when the planes finally left. The telescopes remained in use for decades, with the survivor of the pair part of MERLIN, in conjunction with Jodrell Bank.

The Royal Radar Establishment once again transmuted in name and with additional functions. In 1976 it merged with the Services Electronics Research Laboratory at Baldock and the Signals Research and Development Establishment at Christchurch. The new name was the Royal Signals and Radar Establishment, (RSRE), the headquarters of which became Malvern.

The RSRE now added defence satellite communications to its work, and in 1980 the existing Christchurch function was moved to Defford. The Defford location possessed clear lines of sight to satellites and, being in the 'middle of nowhere', there was both secrecy and minimal electrical interference.

White *'golf balls'*, (real name Geodesic Domes), sprang up along the old east to west runway, protecting the satellite aerial equipment that faced south. One of the radio telescopes, which had previously been engaged in radar meteorology work, a precursor of the Met Office radar 'weather pictures', was adapted for satellite communications. Bredon Hill hosted a satellite payload simulator.

The purpose of a Simulator is to provide a realistic simulation of the satellite or spacecraft, to enable equipment to be set up correctly, facilitate operator-training, cope with special events – e.g. an eclipse, and contingency planning.

Much of the work of Defford from this time revolved around the development and use of satellite communications for military purposes, hence the location's 'Top Secret' status continued.

In the early days of satellite technology, the 1960s, only two countries, the United States and Soviet Union, utilised satellites for signals and military intelligence.

Signals Intelligence is the interception of signals communications between people, or other signals not used for communication, from which intelligence may be obtained.

The UK decided to build its own satellite network, called 'Skynet', which was used for military intelligence communications and encrypted communications for British armed forces. The biggest user of Skynet was Government Communications Headquarters, (GCHQ), in Cheltenham.

There were a number of versions of Skynet satellites built, the first launched in 1969. Skynet 4 was the first fully British built satellite, by British Aerospace Dynamics, the first version being launched in 1988. The satellite communications facility at Defford had a major role in the operation of Skynet for military communications.

Fig 90 *The Defford 'golf balls'*

Defford also continued to host research and performed civilian functions for the British National Space Centre, an agency of the UK Government first formed in 1985.

Also starting at Christchurch, and continuing at Defford, was the development of mobile ground satellite communications systems, both for airborne carriage and deployment, and small enough to be carried by a man as a 'back-pack'. Eventually Defford developed a fully mobile unit based on a prototype contained within two Land Rovers, which was perfected and used in the 1992 Gulf War by the Army. It facilitated secure speech and data transfer through 'frequency hopping', which also hindered any jamming attempts.

Following the changes and amalgamations at Malvern, including the privatisation of certain elements, Defford was transferred to the QinetiQ private company.

When, in 2003, Skynet operation was contracted by the Ministry of Defence to Astrium, a subsidiary of the European Aeronautic Defence and Space Company, which provided civilian and military space systems and services, Defford's role ceased and the satellite facility closed.

Fig 91 The Radio Telescopes on 11 April 2006 prior to the removal of the nearer scope

West Mercia Police later leased the part of the airfield previously occupied by QinetiQ, and the *'golf balls'* and satellite communications equipment were removed. One empty geodesic dome survives, now used for storage. The second, by now redundant radio telescope was removed, together with the rails, leaving the surviving MERLIN linked dish on a short section of rail. This dish is operated by remote control from Jodrell Bank.

A new storage building used by the police is named *'The Sir Bernard Lovell Building'.*

A significant amount of the old runways survive, albeit much deteriorated, with one no more than a car track. The trees have reclaimed the areas that used to be occupied by the many buildings and aircraft dispersal areas, although broken down foundations can be glimpsed through the woods, which are private property.

Fig 92 Aerial view of Defford 2007 showing runways and surviving telescope bottom right. Croome lies off photo to the right

There appear to be remnants of wartime brick buildings within the pig farm near to the airfield entrance, and a glimpse of hangars used for farm purposes can be gained on the regular 'RAF Walk' from Croome. The buildings preserved by the National Trust at Croome Park, and the Defford Heritage Museum, are described later in this chapter.

The past glory and romance has gone forever, although one can still just about imagine a Lancaster or Halifax, covered in aerials and strange bulges, coming in to land.

Fig 93 Defford today – looking along old runway towards Bredon Hill

(Right) *Fig 94* Defford today – looking towards Croome. The trees have reclaimed the land where most of the buildings stood

* * *

'The Monkey House'

Those in search of a taste of nostalgia will be heartened to know that *'The Monkey House'*, mentioned so many times in recollections of Defford, still exists, one of only four traditional cider houses left in the country. The cider is no longer the fearsome and legendary home-brewed liquor from apples in the orchard, being now supplied by a well-known cider maker, but it is still served through a hatch and customers have to sit outside, or in the *'tool shed'* if it rains.

The Sheriffs Lench Observatory

This tiny and little-known site near to Pershore, fast disappearing into the weeds, boasts an impressive story that is worthy of inclusion in this book.

It was originally a VHF station for RAF Pershore, but in the 1950s, a secret purpose linked to RRE at Malvern was initiated.

Fig 95 Local farmer Roger Allard at the Monkey House

In 1955/6, amidst great secrecy, construction began of a massive concrete base, above which was placed a barrack-like structure from Pershore airfield.

This structure housed a 'Ballistic Camera' – a camera designed for the precise photography of trajectories and other features of high velocity flight, using techniques such as high-speed multiple imaging, timed exposure with wide-angle lenses, and calibration against the night sky.

In other words, a means of tracking Inter-Continental Ballistic Missiles.

The camera took photographic evidence of the target object's location, capturing a very accurate optical position, which was compared with co-located radar information, enabling precise radar calibration for tracking purposes.

The Sherrifs Lench site was linked to a sister-site camera at Lye Valletts in Herefordshire, the two locations working together.

During 1957, again covertly, two brick-built single-storey buildings were constructed, along with two seventy-foot high wooden towers on concrete foundations that bore the radar aerial. Also added were a water supply, septic tank, and a diesel powered electricity generator.

This activity took place during the 'Cold War' between the USA and Russia. The launch of the Sputnik satellite on 4 October 1957, observed by RRE via a high-powered radar on a radio telescope at the RRE Staff Club – which is now Morgan Motors Visitor Centre, caused panic in the West at the prospect of the Russians controlling space, and the USA speedily responded by launching the Explorer 1 satellite atop a Juno missile booster on 31 January 1958.

Suddenly, inner-space and satellites were part of the arms race.

RRE at Malvern began developing a satellite-tracking camera, and this work received new impetus when a British medium-range, (1000-3000km), ballistic nuclear deterrent missile project, code-named 'Blue Streak' was announced.

Although extremely successful technically, it was later cancelled in 1960 due to its expense and its vulnerability to a pre-emptive strike. The new camera was designed to track the missile, or missiles. However, development work resulted in an internationally famous telescope called the 'Hewitt Telescope', after its inventor, Joe

Hewitt, being built at the Malvern Engineering Unit and Laboratories. The optical parts were supplied by Grubb & Co, better known as Grubb Parsons, world-famous telescope manufacturers of Newcastle Upon Tyne.

Despite the cancellation of *'Blue Streak'*, the Hewitt Cameras were installed at Sherrifs Lench and Lye Valletts in 1962, for use in satellite tracking, ostensibly for Geodetic Analysis, which is the accurate measurement of the Earth or any planet, i.e. satellite mapping of the Earth's surface.

The telescope was kept in a special hut that incorporated a double-skin to protect it. The hut was mounted on rails so it could be drawn back, exposing the camera. Sensors inside the hut monitored the temperature and automatically cooled it to that of the evening air outside to enable immediate use once exposed.

The Hewitt cameras were the most accurate satellite cameras in the world. The Sherrifs Lench camera operated until 1982 and was then transferred to the Royal Greenwich Observatory at Herstmonceux in Sussex.

It was 'retired' and placed in the museum there in 1990.

The Herefordshire telescope went to Edinburgh in 1964 and then to New South Wales, Australia, in 1982, again retiring in 1990.

The site still bears important remnants of the buildings and bases – and the shed.

A planning application to redevelop the site was rejected in 2015, but its days appear to be numbered unless some funding and

Fig 96 Sherrifs Lench Observatory today – the telescope hut

Fig 97 *Sherrifs Lench Observatory – the rails on which the hut rode to expose the telescope*

plan for its preservation is found, with both hut and buildings suffering much deterioration

Pershore

In 1977 Pershore became part of the RSRE (Royal Signals Radar Establishment) and its direct involvement with aircraft ceased.

Pershore was thus no longer a military airfield and eventually passed from Government ownership to the defence firm *'QinetiQ'* when that company was formed in 2001, having formerly been part of the Defence Evaluation and Research Agency.

QinetiQ still own the site and have a secure facility there.

In 2001, Throckmorton Airfield, as it is locally known, was used as a burial site for the carcasses of over 100,000 animals contaminated by foot and mouth disease.

The site is now called Throckmorton Park and operates as a Business Park hosting a number of companies and as a 'Trials Centre'. The runways are substantially intact and a number of the airfield buildings, including the control tower, remain.

The Park boasts *'320 acres comprising of 3 runways, 2 aprons, 5 hangars, various buildings, a laser range, 4x4 course and vast areas of open space and hard standing'*.

Throckmorton has been used for military research and development trials, police driver training, firework testing and the development of laser measurement equipment. Ironically, in view of its illustrious aviation history, model aeroplanes are flown there.

The site has also been used as a television location. In an echo of its history as a training base, parts of the runway are used by young 'learner drivers' before they are old enough to be taught on the road.

Between 2010 and 2015, the Throckmorton Air Show was run at Pershore but was cancelled in 2016 because of spiralling insurance costs and new Civil Aviation Authority rules.

Fig 98
Pershore Airfield buildings today

Fig 99 *Pershore Airfield buildings today*

Fig 100 *Pershore Airfield buildings today*

Fig 101 *Pershore Airfield buildings today*

Malvern

Following the creation in 1976 of RSRE, the core groups from the merged organisations were centred at Malvern, which became the headquarters and focal point of the new establishment. Originally part of the Air Ministry, the new organization eventually became a part of the Ministry of Defence, becoming The Defence Evaluation and Research Agency, (DERA) in April 1995.

On 1 July 2001, following a defence technology and research privatisation initiative instigated by the Labour government, the major part of the DERA officially became known as QinetiQ, (pronounced kinetic), now a global defence technology company with headquarters in Farnborough.

Many of the original eighty-plus laboratories employing some 9,000 scientists were transferred to the private sector.

DRA/DERA/QinetiQ – Malvern undertook, and in some cases continues to undertake, wide-ranging research including: electronic and device physics, radar detection and electronic warfare (including radar and communications jamming), encryption, computer security, night vision research, secure communications, satellites and data links, stealth and unmanned aerial vehicles technology, and many other areas relevant to defence.

QinetiQ still retains a small facility in Malvern, near to the old *'HMS Duke'* building.

Much of the TRE *'North Site'* is a housing development, although, two roads are named *'TRE Road'* and *'RRDE Road'*, and are linked together by *'Duke Crescent'*.

The UK government retains control of sensitive *'Top Secret'* sections of QinetiQ such as the germ warfare laboratories at Porton Down, Wiltshire.

The original site of TRE, Malvern Boys College, is now Malvern College, a day and boarding school for pupils aged 13-16 years.

Malvern Museum, housed in the Abbey Gateway, once entrance to Great Malvern Priory, contains some memories of the invasion of the *'boffins'*.

However, the modern visitor to Malvern will find a sleepy town, nestling under Elgar's hills, the memories of its once mighty achievements gradually fading.

Croome Court

In 1948, with the Earls having run out of money, the Croome Estate Trust sold the house and 38 acres of land to the Roman Catholic Archdiocese of Birmingham, and the house became St Josephs Special School for 'disadvantaged' boys, run by nuns between 1950 and 1979.

In 1979, the house was taken over by the International Society for Krishna Consciousness, the *'Hare Krishna'* movement, and became their headquarters and training college, called Chaitanya College, run by twenty-five members of the movement.

By 1984 they had run into financial difficulties and left.

Between 1984 and 2007, various enterprises attempted to use the house as a training centre; apartments; a restaurant and conference centre, and a hotel and golf course, before it became a private home with the outbuildings converted to private houses.

The house interiors and grounds deteriorated, with the landscape park lost beneath vegetation.

Fortunately, in 1996, the National Trust were able to acquire the grounds with a Heritage Lottery Fund grant, and commenced restoration of the landscape park, opening it to the public.

The Trust also preserved and refurbished some of the surviving RAF buildings.

In 2007 the house was purchased by the Croome Heritage Trust, a registered charity, and the property is now leased to the National Trust for 999 years.

In 2012, having secured English Heritage funding, they began restoration of the ruined red brick service wing.

More recently, the house has undergone extensive renovation, externally and internally, which continues. Sadly, the contents were dispersed in the various sales, but it now houses various exhibitions and displays.

The site as a whole receives ever-increasing visitor numbers and is fast becoming one of the National Trust's biggest draws.

* * *

'Cold War' Bunkers

The 'Cold War' spawned another series of secret structures across the Worcestershire countryside in the form of underground bunkers ranging in size from a vast complex to tiny observation posts.

The majority were 'mini-bunkers', part of a chain of over 1500, built across Britain and manned by the Royal Observer Corps, the RAF's own *'Territorial Army'*. Their existence was owed to an assumption that the enormous EMP (Electro-Magnetic Pulse), of a nuclear detonation would disable conventional radar, radio communications, and other electronic monitoring equipment, the bunkers being established as an alternative.

They were placed in clusters, as not all were expected to emerge intact from being in the proximity of a nuclear explosion. In fact, as Atom and Hydrogen bomb technology progressed after World War Two, the distance from ground zero required for a bunker's survival rose from 5km to 20km and then to 40km.

The small number of ROC members staffing each bunker were supposed to provide information about oncoming missiles, the location of strikes and the blast intensity to regional nuclear command centres, which would initiate the response of V-bombers and missiles, if these were not destroyed in a first strike.

The survival rate of the ROC monitors was not expected to be high if in the proximity of a nuclear strike. They were also expected to risk ventures to the surface to retrieve information from equipment, and decontamination equipment was limited or absent. It was estimated that two to three weeks would be required for radiation to drop to a level allowing limited human exposure. The bunkers were not equipped with large food reserves and belts would have had to be tightened to eke out the rations.

The instrumentation in these monitoring facilities included:

The BPI Bomb Power Indicator: This looked like a large pressure gauge and was connected to the surface via a metal pipe. Baffles on the surface provided a means of measuring the pressure change from a nuclear detonation as the blast waves passed over them. This information, when combined with the distance to the blast obtained from the GZI, (see below), could be used to measure the kiloton yield. This device was created at Aldermaston Atomic Weapons Research Establishment and calibrated during nuclear tests on Christmas Island.

The GZI Ground Zero Indicator: This was also known as the Shadowgraph. It worked via a surface mounted small metal drum containing four pinhole cameras that were accurately aligned for location and height. A nuclear blast would burn a precise image onto light sensitive paper. An operator was required to retrieve and replace the paper from the surface.

Radiation Measurement: Initially, radiation was measured by a **RSM Radiac Survey Meter**, which used a Geiger Muller Tube. This was largely superseded by the **FSM Fixed Survey Meter** that employed a surface ionization detector protected by a polycarbonate dome. Both of these devices required significant battery power to operate and were eventually replaced by the **PDRM 82 Portable Dose Meter,** which was an improved device, and required only three 1.5 volt batteries.

Teletalk: An obvious technical hurdle was that when the bunkers were first constructed, the ROC staff were supposed to report to the Control Centre via normal telephone lines that were unlikely to survive an attack. Therefore an underground communications system had to be devised which used special cables that were protected against blast damage and EMP disruption.

As the 'Cold War' wound down, a decision was made to sell off or close the ROC posts, commensurate with the discharge of the majority of ROC volunteers in 1991. Many of these mini-bunkers are gone without trace, but a number remain in an abandoned state, or have been preserved or adapted for other uses. The usual visible sign above ground is that of ventilation outlets and small turrets containing the hatch entrance.

The Worcestershire ROC post locations were:

Arley: Opened in April 1961 and closed in October 1968. Located on the East side of Trimpley Lane, near Trimpley Reservoir. Demolished without trace.

Broadway: Opened in June 1960 and closed in September 1991. The bunker lies approximately 300 yards North East of

Broadway Tower and the floor is approximately 6 metres underground. The bunker has been recently restored to its 1991 condition and is open to the public, managed by Broadway Tower and maintained by members of the ROC Association, North Cotswolds Branch. It was constructed in 1959 from reinforced concrete and has its own ventilation and battery back up if mains power fails. Access is via a laddered shaft from an above ground bulkhead with metal door. There are two rooms, the operations room and a toilet. Contained in the main room were two bunk beds, a filing alcove and a desk. The ventilation shafts could be sealed off by metal sliders and instrument readings were obtained from pipes from the surface.

Bromsgrove: Opened August 1961 and closed in October 1968. Situated on a hilltop off Pikes Pool Lane on land owned by The Birmingham Scouts and used as an Activity Centre. Surface structures are still visible but the bunker has been sealed with concrete.

Clows Top: Opened in June 1959 and closed in October 1968. Located near to a public footpath 150 yards South of the A456. Derelict.

Crowle: Opened in June 1959 and closed in October 1968. Located on a mound East of Netherwood Lane. Derelict.

Evesham: Opened in May 1963 and closed in October 1968. Demolished without trace.

Inkberrow: Opened in December 1962 and closed September 1991. Located near to Stone Pit Lane. Abandoned.

Ombersley: Opened in August 1961 and closed in September 1991. Located near to footpath from Stone Bank. Abandoned.

Pershore: Opened in November 1961 and closed in October 1968. Located in a field North of the A44. Abandoned and surface features removed.

Powick: Opened in February 1962 and closed in September 1991. Located near to Kings End Lane. Last reported as lying in a secure compound and used to house communications equipment for a nearby mast.

Redditch: Opened in May 1963 and closed in October 1968. This bunker, on a hill adjoining Weights Lane, overlooking Redditch, was constructed in a mound in a sandpit. Sand extraction has since exposed a good portion and it is derelict.

Upper Sapey: Opened in August 1962 and closed in September 1991. It is located East of the B4204 and is abandoned.

Upton on Severn: Opened in August 1961 and closed in September 1991. It was purchased by ex ROC Chief Observer, Berny Male in 1993 for £500. He is gradually restoring it as a piece of nostalgia and history.

* * *

Non-ROC Secret nuclear facilities in Worcestershire

BBC Wood Norton: Known as PAWN, (Protected Area Wood Norton). The estate of Wood Norton Hall was acquired by the BBC before World War Two as an emergency broadcasting facility and subsequently used as a training centre. Its secret however, is that it was designated as an emergency 'Cold War' broadcasting unit in the event of a nuclear attack, and a bunker to facilitate this function was constructed beneath a new training wing, the Bredon Wing, beginning in 1966.

After a nuclear strike, tape-recorded programmes would have been broadcast in an attempt to promote calm and bolster morale.

It is said that at one time, 100 days worth of broadcasts were ready, including *'The Sound of Music'*, although it is difficult to imagine that listening to *'My Favourite Things'* would have lightened the mood much after a nuclear war.

The existence of the bunker was 'Top Secret' and it is said that the BBC employees aware of its existence had to sign the Official Secrets Act. As recently as 2015, it was rumoured that the facility was still preserved and secured, and a Freedom of Information Request produced the following response from the BBC:

> 'In regards to Protected Area Wood Norton it is the BBC's Policy that in the interest of National Security we cannot comment or provide information on locations that currently form part of the emergency broadcast network'.

Drakelow Tunnels: This underground facility, beneath the Kingsford Country Park, near Kidderminster, was originally constructed in 1941 as a 'shadow factory' for the Rover company, which manufactured aircraft engines at the time. There are over three miles of tunnels. Aircraft engine parts were manufactured there during the war, and tanks afterwards. In the 1950s, the site was used for storage by the Ministry of Supply.

Approximately half of the complex became a 'Cold War' facility in 1958 when it was designated and developed as a Regional Seat of Government, (RSG9), in the event of nuclear conflict. Subsequently, the bunker became Sub-Regional Control, (SRC), Sub-Regional Headquarters, (SRHQ), and eventually Regional Government Headquarters, (RGHQ). As recently as the 1980s the site was classed as 'Top Secret' and was modernised with the addition of blast doors and airlocks to upgrade it into a full nuclear facility. It was decommissioned and sold in 1993.

The tunnels enjoyed a rather more colourful reputation after government ownership ended when police discovered a sophisticated cannabis factory containing many hundreds of cannabis plants in one of the tunnels, resulting in a conviction.

The Drakelow Tunnels Preservation Trust has been restoring the complex to its original condition as a Cold War Museum. It is the largest underground space open to the public in the UK. An informative website exists at www.drakelow-tunnels.co.uk.

'Top Secret' documentation relating to the operation of Drakelow is still being released and it is thought that much still remains classified.

Pershore Airfield Battle HQ Bunker: Opened in February 1962 and closed in September 1991. It was demolished, no trace remains.

Honeybourne Airfield Battle HQ Bunker: No opening and closing dates available. It was demolished without trace.

The 'Cold War' structures of the United Kingdom, many of which were relatively recently in use, are fast fading away and the efforts of those who restore and reopen these pieces of history are important for future generation's knowledge of this fascinating era.

* * *

Keeping The Memories Alive

Over the years a band of dedicated individuals have sought to preserve the history of Defford Airfield in particular.

For example, an annual RAF Defford Reunion took place at Croome Court on Saturday 17 July 2010, at the same time as the National Trust's, *'RAF Defford at 70,'* themed weekend at Croome Park.

Guests saw displays that included an introduction to the newly-formed Defford Airfield Heritage Group, and the display of a scale-model of RAF Defford, made by Albert Shorrock, who served there in the RAF during World War Two as an airframe fitter, from 1942 onwards.

Mike McDonald, son of Group Captain McDonald, presented a framed copy of the David Shepherd painting *'Spitfire EN915'* to the group. He spoke of his father's time as Station Commander and his *'hands on'* approach to piloting the planes used for radar trials and development.

In September 2011 the Defford Airfield Heritage Group merged with the RAF Defford Reunion Association.

Huge efforts have been made by the Defford Airfield Heritage Group and the National Trust at Croome to keep the memories of the airfield alive. By way of another example, on 14 Saturday September 2013 an RAF Heritage weekend took place at Defford which included a planned fly-past by the Red Arrows display team and a Lancaster Bomber.

Building work started in the spring of 2014 on the restoration of the surviving Decontamination Annexe of RAF Defford in Croome Park, to accommodate the RAF Defford Museum.

The restoration work was funded by a grant from *'Severn Waste Serves'* based in Evesham, through the Landfill Community Scheme.

Fig 102
Lancaster over Croome 2013

The building was formally handed over to the National Trust at Croome on the 16 May 2014, by the contractors, '*Croft Building and Conservation*'.

Externally the building was restored to its 1942 appearance, but adapted internally to house the museum exhibits.

Also in May 2014, Defford Airfield Heritage Group were notified that they had been awarded an, '*Our Heritage*', grant of £82,900 by the Heritage Lottery Fund to fund the interior of the buildings and a three-year outreach programme.

On the 12 July 2014, there was a Defford Airfield Day with a planned fly-past by a Dakota aircraft.

At the end of July 2014, one '*explorer*', with an eye for conspiracy theories, speculated on Facebook as to what secret work was still being undertaken at Defford, following the discovery of a large crop circle in a wheat-field adjacent to it, and no apparent footsteps in its vicinity – an English, '*Area 51*', perhaps?

The museum opened on Sunday 28 September 2014, and members of the Defford Airfield Heritage Group have played an active role in an outreach and educational programme targeting schools, colleges, and universities.

A second former RAF building, the Ambulance Garage and Mortuary, was restored with funding from a private donor and this was opened in February 2016.

This building houses the cockpit and forward fuselage of an English Electric Canberra, which was used as an RRE grounded training simulator at RRE Pershore.

The former Mortuary houses the Museum store.

* * *

On the 9 July 2016, well-known 1940s singer Jayne Darling formed part of the line-up at the Defford Airfield Heritage Day with plans for a fly-past by Spitfire P7350, part of the Battle of Britain Memorial Flight, plus a Hurricane.

Between September 2014 and August 2016, the museum received 100,000 visitors through its doors.

* * *

Maggie Doyle, Croome Poet, and ex Worcestershire Poet Laureate Emeritus, wrote a poem about the Men's Ward at RAF Defford, where aircrew and other members of staff recovered from minor injuries and ailments.

This surviving Defford airfield hospital building now houses the restaurant at National Trust Croome, and a number of pictures and posters on the walls recreate the wartime atmosphere. The lights in the restaurant originally hung over the hospital beds.

Secrets of Croome

Hidden in woodland, trying to make sense of science,
we each have our role to play. War seems so far away
as we carry on with everyday tasks, gas masks
giving the only clue as to what may happen.
Here, we ensure our aircrews are fit for war.
Here, frustration, elation, excitement and fear are bedfellows.
Some patients have experienced the thrill
of battles in the sky as others wonder why

a burst ear drum takes so long to heal.
Richard can't wait to fly again, twitches at the thought.
Ernest imagines life at home, no more war;
both will re-capture the skies, given time.

Fig 103 Maggie
Doyle at Croome

Lincolnshire Aviation Heritage Centre

The stunning photographs in this book, of the Lancaster bomber and the H2S equipment it bears, were provided by the Lincolnshire Aviation Heritage Centre, and its official photographer, Martin Keen.

The centre is in East Kirkby, Lincolnshire and was opened in 1988 by Lincolnshire farmers Fred and Harold Panton, as a memorial to their older brother, Christopher Witton Panton, who died during World War Two.

The brothers acquired an Avro Lancaster Mk VII, NX611, and part of the redundant RAF East Kirkby airfield, and the site now houses historic aircraft with other owners, and related exhibits.

However, the focus is the Lancaster, named 'Just Jane' after the very popular wartime adult comic strip character 'Jane'. The plane was brought to the airfield in 1987, renovated and now can be booked for 'taxi rides' around the airfield, raising funds for its maintenance and restoration. We are privileged to publish photographs of this magnificent survivor.

Fig 104 Just Jane

Fig 105 Just Jane

The 'Ultimate Sacrifice'

Pershore Cemetery in Worcestershire contains the remains of forty-one Canadian airmen from Pershore and Defford, who died during World War Two. The majority lie in a war-graves plot leased and maintained by the Commonwealth War Graves Commission. At the northern end of the cemetery stands the Cross of Sacrifice between two Canadian Maple trees, sent from Canada as a gift.

The Commission looks after a total of seventy-four graves on the site, of which sixty-four are those of airmen.

A service of Remembrance takes place on the 11 November each year at the Cross of Sacrifice, and the names of the fallen are read out on alternative years.

Among the headstones is that of Flying Officer G.S. Hynam DFC, who died whilst taking part in a fly-past over Pershore Town in May 1943 when his Wellington bomber lost a wing and crashed, damaging the town's *'Brandy Cask'* public house.

He was aged just twenty-two years at the time.

Plot Q, grave 390, is that of Sergeant Bernard Richard Minson, Royal Canadian Air Force, who died on 24 November 1943, aged 27, whilst testing radar in a USAF Liberator flown from Defford.

Each grave commemorates a sacrifice of young lives.

Fig 106
Headstone of Flying Officer G.S. Hynam DFC

Fig 107 *Cross of Sacrifice Canadian War Graves, Pershore cemetery*

* * *

On Tuesday September 10, 2002, a memorial to those who lost their lives whilst engaged with the Telecommunications Flying Unit at Defford was unveiled by Sir Bernard Lovell.

It stands on the Defford village green and represents the fruition of lobbying by the RAF Defford Reunion Association, which is now part of the Defford Airfield Heritage Group.

* * *

The Goodrich Castle Radar Memorial Window

The memorial window, unveiled on the 7th June 1992, the fiftieth anniversary of the disastrous Halifax crash, commemorates the many Service and civilian crews who lost their lives in radar development flying duties between 1936 and 1976.

The memorial comprises a three light stained glass window and a bronze dedicatory plaque.

Light one, on the left, contains a leek, the emblem of Wales, and a rose, the emblem of England at the top. Below is the crest of the Aeroplane and Armament Experimental Establishment at Martlesham, a wartime testing base, and a *'Chain Home Radar'* mast depicted at the bottom centre.

Light two has a Royal Air Force Crest at the top and a diagram of a Cavity Magnetron, the invention that powered the H2S Radar, below it. Also in this light is the Royal Radar Establishment's Coat of Arms, and the crest of the RAF Telecommunications Flying Unit 1941–55.

Light three, on the right, contains the thistle of Scotland and Clover of Ireland at the top, below this the crest of the RAF Radar Research Flying Unit, and at the bottom, an image of a Halifax bomber representing the *'Centimetric'* Airborne Radar.

The dedication states:

> 'This Memorial window, unveiled on the 7th June 1992, commemorates the many Service and civilian aircrews who lost their lives in radar development flying duties between 1936 and 1976.
>
> The Radar Research Squadron's parent Establishment created between 1935 and 1939 the World's first radar managed defence system. This was fundamental to our victory at the Battle of Britain in 1940, and was one of the many British systems to transform air power and earn the nation's gratitude.
>
> The unveiling marks the anniversary of the worst tragedy when a Halifax aircraft carrying the prototype of the first ever ground mapping radar bombing aid crashed near Goodrich Castle, killing all eleven on board. This navigational bombing aid made possible effective strategic air power while its

Fig 108 *The TFU Memorial Defford*

Fig 109
*Goodrich Castle
memorial
window light*

maritime derivative saved the British Isles from total isolation by submarines. Together both versions allowed the assembly of large military resources in Britain that enabled the Allies to liberate Europe in 1944/45.

They applied the frontier of scientific knowledge to the salvation of their country.'

* * *

The Alan Blumlein Plaque

Alan Blumlein is commemorated at Defford Airfield today. A building occupied by West Mercia Police is called *'The Alan Blumlein Building'* and bears both a plaque and a dedication with photograph of him.

In February 2017, Blumlein received further recognition with the announcement of a posthumous *'Grammy'* award as a *'special merit recipient'* in recognition of his invention of *'binaural sound'*, which we now know as *'stereo'*.

Finally perhaps, Alan Dower Blumlein, war-hero and inventor, is gaining the fame he so richly deserves.

* * *

In writing this book the authors realised that whether flying, or maintaining a plane, or developing a new invention, the lives of the people who lived and worked at Defford, Pershore and Malvern over the years were inextricably linked.

Whether they were pilots, scientists, aircrews, firemen, aircraft fitters, members of the WAAF or people who worked in the NAAFI – they have all earned, and justly deserve, pride of place in the *'Top Secret'* history of Worcestershire.

Fig 110 *A hint of the past at Defford entrance*

This is a prohibited place within the meaning of the Official Secrets Act Unauthorised persons entering the area may be arrested and prosecuted

Authors' Note

Writing a book of this nature requires a balance between giving an accurate and sufficiently detailed account of the critical aspects of historical record, whilst making the text accessible to a wider readership. The authors have taken all reasonable steps to ensure accuracy and completeness. However, some 70 years or more after the main events occurred, the use of primarily secondary and personal sources inevitably results in alternative views being available.

If any reader is willing to share further recollections and photographs of any of the locations or subject matter featured in this book, please contact the authors via our Facebook page, 'Bostin Books'. (www.facebook.com/BostinBooks).

Photographs and Illustrations

The authors are extremely grateful to the following individuals and organisations for their kind permission to use their photographs and illustrations in this book:

Malvern Museum and Robert Fisher (The Douglas Fisher Archive): Figures 1, 2, 45, 46, 47, 48, 49, 50, 51, 52, 56, 57, 58, 59, 60, 61, 69, 88, 89

Paul Dallimore: Figures 10, 11, 12, 13, 14, 15, 16, 17, 18, 19, 20, 21, 22, 70, 71, 72, 73, 74, 75, 76, 77, 78, 79, 80, 81, 87

Peter Clarke: Figures 24, 25, 26, 27, 28, 29, 30, 31, 32, 33, 34, 35, 36, 37, 38, 39, 40, 41, 42

Lincolnshire Aviation Heritage Centre and Silksheen Photography: Figures 6, 9, 53, 54, 55, 104, 105

Simon and Sheila Young: Figures 62, 63, 64, 65, 66

Steve Davis Country Shots Photography: Figures 98, 99, 100, 101

Chris Pell: Figures 3, 67, 68

Dave Haffenden: Figures 4, 5

Society of Merchant Venturers as Trustee of St Monica Trust: Figures 93, 94

Martyn Jones: Figures 96, 97

Dave Bowen: Figure 7

Stephen Rendle via Vickers Viscount network.png: Figure 82

Colin Bryan: Figure 83

Philip David Read: Figure 84

Bill Lowe: Figure 85
David Ball: Figure 86
Philip Halling: Figure 90
Martin Swift: Figure 91
John Chorley: Figure 92
Stewart Bourne: Figure 102
Maggie Doyle: Figure 103
English Heritage: Figure 109

Bibliography

'Aircraft for Airborne Radar Development' (1988) W.H. Sleigh (Archive and Library Section, RAF Museum Hendon reference number 023235)

'Canadians On Radar Royal Canadian Air Force 1949-45' George K. Grande, Sheila M. Linden & Horace R. Macaulay (Canadian Radar History Project online publication)

'Echoes of War – The Story of H2S Radar' (1991) Sir Bernard Lovell

'Fifty Years Of The Cavity Magnetron' (February 1990) University of Birmingham

'Introduction to Radio Astronomy' Dr R.C. Jennison

'Most Secret War' (Penguin 1978) R.V. Jones

'Pioneers of Radar' (Sutton Publishing 1999) Colin Latham and Anne Stobbs

'Radar Days' (1987) E.G. 'Taffy' Bowen

'Radio Astronomy' (1960) Francis Graham-Smith

'Radio Astronomy Report' (1961-5 – Vol 7) Proceedings of Observatories (Royal Astronomical Society)

'Science comes to Malvern – TRE a Story of Radar 1942-1953' (2009) Ernest Putley

'The Endless Sky – Pershore and Defford' (1988) Glyn Warren

'The Inventor of Stereo: The Life and Works of Alan Blumlein' Robert Alexander

'New Scientist Magazine' (4.1.62) article by Dr Hey

'The Invention of The Cavity Magnetron' Physics in Canada Nov/Dec 2001 Paul. A. Redhead

'Top Secret Boeing' (2012) Bob Shaw for Defford Airfield Heritage Group

Acknowledgements and References

Michael Allard – son of Roger Allard
Roger Allard – local farmer in Defford area
Colin Bryan – retired British Transport Police Officer
Peter Clarke – Worcestershire resident
Dave Coombe – retired West Mercia Police Officer
Paul Dallimore – son of Thomas James Dallimore
Maggie Doyle – Croome Poet, and ex Worcestershire Poet Laureate Emeritus
Derek Hackett – retired police officer
Dave Haffenden – retired West Midlands Police Officer and son of Walter Haffenden
John Harris – son of Norman Harris
Gordon Leith – Curator (Archive & Library Section) The RAF Museum Hendon
William Charles Lowe – retired MOD Fire Officer
Chris Pell – Scientist and scientific advisor on this book
Philip David Read – retired mechanic RAF Pershore
Sheila Young née Marchant MBE – wife of David John Young
Simon Young – retired West Mercia Police Officer and son of David John Young

* * *

Airfield Research Group
Defford Airfield Heritage Group
English Heritage
Lincs Aviation Heritage Centre
Malvern Museum

ACKNOWLEDGEMENTS AND REFERENCES

Malvern Radar and Technology History Group
National Trust – Croome
Archive and Library Section, RAF Museum Hendon (London)

* * *

Air Images Britain
Air-Scene UK magazine (2006)
BBC Midlands Today (May 2008) and BBC Hereford & Worcester
    (24.9.2014) programmes
Britain's Cold War. www.thecoldwar.co.uk
Broadway Tower. www.broadwaytower.co.uk
DAHG Twitter Account
'E-Merlin' website – www.e-merlin.ac.uk
'First Cambridge Catalogue of Radio Sources' (1950) Martin Ryle
'2C – The Second Cambridge Catalogue of Radio Sources' (1955)
'3C – The Third Cambridge Catalogue of Radio Sources' (1959)
'Friends of Croome' online newsletters & Oral Memories Project run
    by Eileen Clement
History Website.co.uk – article by Dr Carl Chinn
Leaflet – *'Royal Radar Establishment Open Day'* at Pershore –
    (18.5.1963) (Malvern Museum)
Letter from Beryl Meakin (Archive and Library Section, RAF
    Museum Hendon reference number X002-9358/005/003)
RAF Defford Inspection 1948 (Archive and Library Section, RAF
    Museum Hendon reference number X003-6195/003)
RAF Pershore Dance invitation (Archive and Library Section, RAF
    Museum Hendon reference number X004-1475/022)
Royal Observer Corps Association. www.roc-heritage.co.uk
Subterranea Britannica. www.subbrit.org.uk
The Telegraph Obituary (22 October 2007) relating to Harry Scott
    DSO, DFC and Bar
'WR Magazine' – Autumn/Winter edition (2016) – article by Pippa
    Sanderson
Wikipedia
Worcester News: Article re Upton on Severn ROC post and Berny
    Male (Mike Pryce)

Glossary of Terms

Air Defence Research & Development Establishment (ADRDE)

Air-Interception Radar – the radar used in night-fighters to detect enemy aircraft (AI)

Air to Surface Vessel – used for detection of ships & submarines (ASV)

Airborne Gun Laying In Turrets (AGLT)

Air Controlled Interception (ACI)

Air Training Corps (ATC)

Air Ministry Experimental Station (AMES)

Air Ministry Research Establishment (AMRE)

Aix: Sophisticated 3cm ASV

Army Operational Research Group (AORG)

Ash: Pod – mounted ship detection radar mounted on anti-shipping aircraft.

Airborne Warning and Control System (AWACS)

Beam Approach Beacon System (BABS)

Blind Navigation (BN)

Boozer: British radar detection device designed to assess ability of Wurtzburg fire controlled radar to detect small aircraft such as Mosquito bombers

Bomb Power Indicator (BPI)

Breadboard – an experimental electronic circuit mounted on any handy piece of board

British Branch of the Radiation Laboratory (BBRL)

Centimetre radar – radar with a wavelength of 10cm or less, allowing a narrow beam to be projected which avoided confusing ground echoes

'Chain Home' – the network of radar stations on the east and south coasts of England for detecting enemy bombers. Played a vital role in winning the Battle of Britain (CH)

The Defence Evaluation And Research Agency (DERA)

Entertainments National Service Association (ENSA)

Elementary Flying Training School (EFTS)

Electromagnetic (EM)

Electromagnetic Pulse (EMP)

Electrical and Musical Instruments Ltd (EMI)

Extremely Low Frequency (ELF)

East-Asian VLBI Network (EAVN)

Fishpond – Bomber tail warning system of approaching enemy night-fighters

Fixed Survey Meter (FSM)

Navigation and Bombing aid (GEE)

Blind Bombing & Precision Navigation (GEE-H)

General Electric Company (GEC)

Government Communications Headquarters (GCHQ)

His Master's Voice Gramophone Company (HMV)

Ground Controlled Interception (GCI)

Ground Zero Indicator (GZI)

H2S – the navigational and blind-bombing radar used by RAF night bombers in WWII

H2X – American version of 3cm H2S system

Identification Friend or Foe (IFF)

International Western Electric (IWE)

K-Band – radar using a wavelength of 1.5cm

Klystron – a form of vacuum tube for the generation and amplification of microwaves

Long Range Navigation System (LORAN)

Magnetron (Cavity) – a device that powerfully generated centimetre wavelength microwaves

Mandrel – Airborne Radar Jammer

Massachusetts Institute of Technology, Boston, seat of American wartime radar design (MIT)

Microwave Early Warning Radar (MEW)

Multi Element Radio-Linked Interferometer Network (MERLIN)

Multi Telescope Radio-Linked Interferometer (MTRLI)

Metox – a U-Boat listening device to detect ASV

Ministry of Aircraft Production Research Establishment (MAPRE)

Ministry of Aircraft Production Guard Dog School (MAPGDS)

Ministry of Defence (MOD)

Ministry of Aircraft Production (MAP)

Monica: Tail warning receiver designed to pick up radar traces of German night fighter closing from rear of a bomber, replaced by Fishpond

Moonshine: Produced a false picture of planes on enemy radar screens

Mandrel: Jamming device for German ground based radar to prevent their night fighters intercepting British bombers

Navigation and Bombing Computer (NBC)

Operations Training Unit (OTU)

OBOE – A radar bombing aid coupled with a beacon transmitter

Passive Infra-Red (PIR)

Plan Position Indicator on a cathode ray tube display – giving a plan view of an area with radar echoes shown in the centre of the screen (PPI)

Portable Dose Meter (PDRM82)

Protected Area Wood Norton (PAWN)

Radiac Survey Meter (RSM)

Radio Direction Finding – the early name for radar (RDF)

Radio Frequencies (RF)

Radar – radio direction and range

Rebecca H: Blind navigation device

Regional Government Headquarters (RGHQ)

Royal Canadian Air Force (RCAF)

Royal Naval Section (RNS)

Royal Observer Corps (ROC)

Radar Research Flying Unit (RRFU)

Radar Research and Development Establishment (RRDE)

Radar Research Establishment (RRE) which later became the Royal Radar Establishment

Royal Signals and Radar Establishment (RSRE)

ROTOR – UK Air Defence Radar System

Satellite Landing Ground (SLG)

Secondary Surveillance Radar (SSR)

Senior Medical Officer (SMO)

Serrate: Fighter radar device that picked up emissions from German night fighters

Special Installation Unit (SIU)

Square Kilometre Array Organisation (SKA)

Sub-Regional Control (SRC)

Sub-Regional Headquarters (SRHQ)

Telecommunications Research Establishment (TRE)

Telecommunications Flying Unit (TFU)

Underground communications system. (Teletalk)

United States Air Force (USAF)

Very Long Base-Line Interferometry (VLBI)

Village Inn: Radar controlled rear gun turret requiring no visible sight of target by gunner

Walter: A tiny mast and battery in a pilot's seat pack which enabled an airborne Rebecca Unit to detect a pilot in the sea following 'bale out'

Window: Thin metal strips of black painted aluminium foil 26.5cm long used to confuse enemy radar into 'seeing' more planes than actually present

Womens Auxiliary Air Force (WAAF)

Womens Royal Naval Section (WRNS)

X-Band – 3 cm wavelength radar